MATHEMATICAL
PUZZLES AND PASTIMES

AARON BAKST

D. VAN NOSTRAND COMPANY, INC.
TORONTO   NEW YORK   LONDON

NEW YORK
D. Van Nostrand Company, Inc., 250 Fourth Avenue, New York 3

TORONTO
D. Van Nostrand Company (Canada), Ltd., 25 Hollinger Rd., Toronto

LONDON
Macmillan & Company, Ltd., St. Martin's Street, London, W.C. 2

03552a35
PRINTED IN THE UNITED STATES OF AMERICA

To
PAMELA SUE

PREFACE

Mathematical recreations have a special place in the mathematical literature. They also have a special place in mathematical pursuits. Generally, recreation is a diversion, or a digression from those activities which represent everyday work, whatever form this work may take. A recreational activity is supposed to be in a lighter vein. In almost every field of human endeavor there is a time and place when the serious surrenders itself to the more or less flippant. Thus, we find relaxation in a jest or a joke. Some have, however, the mistaken notion that mathematics does not lend itself to relaxation. Mathematics, tradition holds, is strait-laced.

The aim of this book is to dispel the idea that mathematics cannot be relaxing. Mathematical recreations, as viewed by the author, are a mathematical approach to a situation which involves the curious, the strange, the unusual, and often the seemingly impossible. Mathematical recreations may be thought of as permitting mathematics to let down its hair. This, however, does not mean that mathematical principles are sacrificed. Such principles are meticulously preserved, although they are simplified. Thus, the bite, which frightens most, is painlessly removed.

The present volume differs from the earlier work of the author, *Mathematics, Its Magic and Mastery* in many respects. In that book, the author's aim was directed toward the development of elementary mathematics in a light vein with considerable emphasis on the versatility of mathematics. The present volume represents a systematic discussion

v

of various mathematical recreations with the view toward developing and systematizing the methods for the solution and treatment of recreational material.

The author does not lay any claims to originality of subject matter. Any originality found here is related to the treatment of the various topics.

New York,   A. B.
April 1954.

CONTENTS

Chapter I

THESE MATCHES ARE NOT FOR BURNING

Many interesting geometric tricks and games may be devised with matchsticks or toothpicks. These games are usually based on the fact that the pieces of wood are all of the same length, although some problems require that some of the pieces be broken into equal lengths. Unless it is specifically stated, however, it is assumed that the pieces of wood are all equal in length.

It is impossible either to formulate a general theory of a Toothpick Geometry or to state the rules for the solutions of matchstick and toothpick problems. With practice, however, one can develop the knack for solving and formulating them. The general idea is simple. A geometric figure is constructed of a certain number of pieces of wood. Then some of the pieces are removed, added, or moved around so that another figure or combination of figures is made. Some of the problems can be solved only by trial and error; others may be solved after a certain amount of reflection. Trying to imagine the new figure often helps to get the answer.

The following problems are arranged according to their difficulty and complexity. The reader is advised to attempt to solve these problems according to their sequence. Although the solutions to these problems are given at the end of the book, a restraint from the natural inclination "to peek" is highly recommended.

After a comparatively limited amount of practice, the reader will develop skill in solving these problems. Moreover, he will discover that he will be able to construct his own problems. Each problem listed in this chapter allows many variations.

PROBLEMS

1. Place 3 toothpicks beside one another as shown in Figure 1. Move them around so they form a double of the figure.

Fig. 1

2. With 4 toothpicks which have been placed alongside one another, construct the triple of this figure.
3. With 11 toothpicks obtain 1.
4. With 12 toothpicks construct a figure like the one shown in Figure 2. Now remove 2 toothpicks, leaving 2 squares.

Fig. 2

5. In Figure 2 transpose 4 toothpicks to construct three squares.
6. Figure 3 contains 17 toothpicks. Remove 5 toothpicks, leaving 3 equal squares.

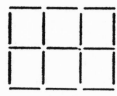

Fig. 3

7. By removing 2 toothpicks from the design in Figure 3, make 6 squares.

8. Remove 4 toothpicks from the design in Figure 4, to make 5 squares.

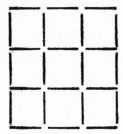

Fig. 4

9. Make 2 squares by removing 8 toothpicks from Figure 4.

10. Remove 8 or 12 toothpicks from Figure 4 so that 3 squares are left.

11. Transpose 8 toothpicks in Figure 4 to construct 3 squares.

12. Remove 8 toothpicks from Figure 4, leaving only 4 squares.

13. From Figure 4, remove 4 toothpicks to make 5 squares.

14. By removing 6 toothpicks from Figure 4, construct 3 squares.

15. Remove 8 toothpicks from the same figure so that 2 squares remain.

16. Make 2 squares by removing 10 toothpicks from Figure 4.

17. Figure 5 consists of 20 toothpicks. Transpose 7 of these to make 2 pairs of equal squares.

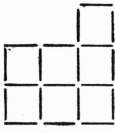

Fig. 5

18. Construct 6 equal four-sided figures (quadrilaterals) by moving 6 of the toothpicks in Figure 6.
19. Remove 5 toothpicks from Figure 6 to form 5 triangles.
20. From the same figure, remove 6 toothpicks so that 5 triangles remain.

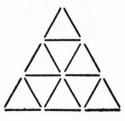

Fig. 6

21. Using 18 toothpicks it is possible to make up 2 rectangular figures (Figure 7) so that the area of one is twice the area of the other. Note that these figures do not have common sides. Using the same 18 toothpicks form 2 four-sided figures so that the area of one is three times that of the other.

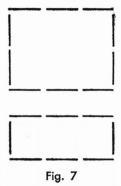

Fig. 7

22. Using 50 toothpicks construct 2 rectangular figures so that the area of one is 2⅔ times the area of the other.
23. With 12 toothpicks construct a figure which is divided into 6 equal areas.

24. Transpose 4 toothpicks in Figure 8 to make 3 equilateral (equal-sided) triangles.

25. Construct 6 four-sided figures (quadrilaterals) by transposing 3 toothpicks in Figure 8.

Fig. 8

26. In Figure 9 transpose 6 toothpicks to form 6 equal four-sided figures (quadrilaterals).

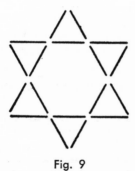

Fig. 9

27. Remove 14 toothpicks from Figure 10 so that 6 equal squares are left.

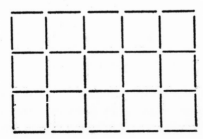

Fig. 10

28. From Figure 11, remove 8 toothpicks so that the remaining figure consists of 6 squares.

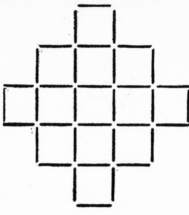

Fig. 11

29. Remove 4 toothpicks from Figure 11 so that 9 squares remain.
30. Make 9 equal squares by removing 8 toothpicks from Figure 11.
31. Remove 24 toothpicks from the design in Figure 12 so that 9 equal squares are left.

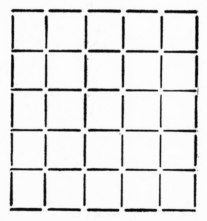

Fig. 12

32. In Figure 13 remove 16 toothpicks to leave 12 equal squares.

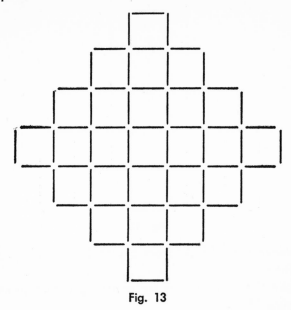

Fig. 13

33. Remove 32 toothpicks from the same figure so that only 6 squares are left.

34. Construct 2 squares by transposing 3 toothpicks in Figure 14.

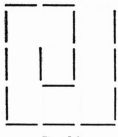

Fig. 14

35. Remove 22 toothpicks from Figure 15 to leave 4 equal squares.

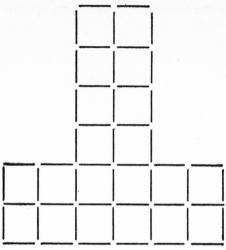

Fig. 15

The foregoing toothpick (or matchstick) problems are just a small sample of the geometrical exercises and puzzlers that can be developed with such materials. If the reader wishes, he may formulate similar problems at his leisure. There isn't any hard-and-fast rule for developing these problems. Construct any figure, regardless how simple or complicated. Then play with it. Remove or transpose some pieces of wood to get new configurations. While you do this, keep track of the changes you are making. If you are absent-minded or forgetful, jot down the various steps so that you will be able to reconstruct your operations.

Problems with toothpicks (or matchsticks) need not be confined to figures in the plane. The following problem will illustrate this idea.

36. With 6 toothpicks construct 4 equilateral (equal-sided) triangles.

Fig. 16

This problem can never be solved by placing all the tooth-picks on the table. Three of the pieces must be made to form a triangle on the table. The remaining three are placed so that one end of each of them touches the vertex of the triangle and the other ends are brought together. The resulting configuration is a pyramid or tetrahedron, a three-dimensional figure with four triangular faces.

If you are ever invited to a party, do not hesitate to take a box of toothpicks with you. More often than not you will receive a repeat invitation.

Chapter 2

A BILLIARD BALL COMPUTER

How to Become an Expert at Pocket Billiards

A pocket billiards expert can perform feats which often are astounding. To make an ordinary shot in pocket billiards requires good eyesight and coordination; but to make a ball go into a certain pocket, after this ball has rebounded from several cushions, is a feat which the ordinary player finds difficult to achieve. To send a cue ball bouncing off several cushions without hitting any other but the desired ball is something which requires skill, mastery and, perhaps, luck.

The game of billiards, strange as it may seem, is based on very sound mathematics. An expert at billiards may insist that he does not know any mathematics and that mathematics was a subject which he hated most in school and in which he was a failure. Although a billiard player may not know mathematics, the mathematical bases of the game are not to be denied and surely not to be disregarded.

An ivory billiard ball rebounds smartly when it hits a cushion of a billiard table. In its rebound it behaves in accord with a physical law that can be stated in mathematical terms. This law, known as *The Law of Incidence and Reflection,* governs the behavior of a rebounding billiard ball just as it does a ray of light.

The law of incidence and reflection, stated in mathematical terms, describes the behavior of a ray when it strikes a reflecting surface. If this ray strikes the surface at some angle α, it is reflected at the same angle. In other words, the law of incidence and reflection is

Angle of incidence $=$ Angle of reflection

If the ray AB strikes the reflecting surface MN at the angle α (see Figure 17), it will be reflected at the same angle, α. However, if the ray strikes the same surface perpendicularly, along the straight line BD perpendicular to MN, it is reflected along the same straight line BD.

The law of incidence and reflection holds good in the game of billiards. If a billiard ball hits the cushion at some

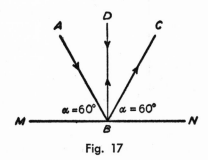

Fig. 17

angle α, it will rebound from the cushion at the same angle α. With the law of incidence and reflection in mind, it is possible to formulate some of the mathematical principles which govern playing billiards. Before these principles are formulated, however, let us examine some interesting cases which may occur while this game is played.

Suppose a billiard ball is placed in the center of a pocket billiards table. It is required to send this ball to one cushion so that it will rebound, hit another cushion, rebound from this cushion, and then, after the third rebound, land in a corner pocket. This is illustrated in Figure 18. How must one strike this ball so that it will follow the prescribed routes?

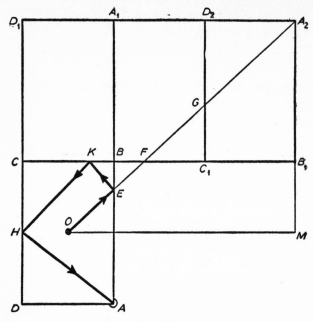

Fig. 18

We shall examine this problem geometrically. Let us rotate the surface of the billiard table through 180° around
the side BC, as shown in Figure 18. The top of the table
will then assume the position CBA_1D_1. Now, let us rotate
the top CBA_1D_1 through 180° around the side A_1B. The
top of the table will then assume the position $A_1BC_1D_2$.
Finally, let us rotate the top $A_1BC_1D_2$ through 180° around
the side C_1D_2. The third position of the top will be
$A_2B_1C_1D_2$. Join the points O (the center of the billiard table
where the billiard ball is located) and A_2 with a straight
line. Extend the straight line A_2B_1, and through the point
O draw a straight line parallel the straight line CBC_1B_1 until it intersects the extension of the straight line A_2B_1 in the
point M. We thus obtain a triangle OA_2M.

The following pairs of triangles are congruent (that is,
their side and their angles are respectively equal):

Triangle KBE is congruent to Triangle BFE

Triangle CHK is congruent to Triangle FC_1G

Triangle AHD is congruent to Triangle GD_2A_2

These triangles come from the triangles found in the original position of the billiard table. The following straight line segments are equal:

$$KE = EF, \quad KH = FG, \quad \text{and} \quad HA = GA_2$$

It follows, then, that:

$$OE + EK + KH + HA = OE + EF + FG + GA_2 = OA_2$$

Since $OE + EK + KH + HA$ represents the length of the path of the billiard ball from the center of the billiard table to the pocket A, sending the ball to the first cushion from which it must rebound requires that the cue stick be aimed in the direction of OA_2, that is, in the direction in which the pocket A would lie if the top of the table were turned over as described above.

Since OM is equal to $2.5AD$, line A_2M equals $1.5AB$. The regulation dimensions of the American pocket billiard table are 10 feet 2 inches and 5 feet and 6 inches between cushions. For the purposes of our computation, we shall assume that the width of the table is approximately 3/5 of the length. This will introduce no serious error, because we are assuming pocket A is a point, although each pocket actually has an aperture of not less than 4 inches. For our purposes, then, AD is equal to $3/5AB$. If we substitute the relation between AD and AB in the expressions $OM = 2.5AD$ and $A_2M = 1.5AB$, we learn that $OM = A_2M$. The triangle A_2OM is, then, an isosceles right triangle, and the angle OEA is equal to 45°. Thus, when the billiard ball is placed at the center of the table, the cue should be aimed at an angle of 45° toward the first cushion. If the billiard ball were placed at a random location on the table, the principle described above would still hold. If the ball is placed off the

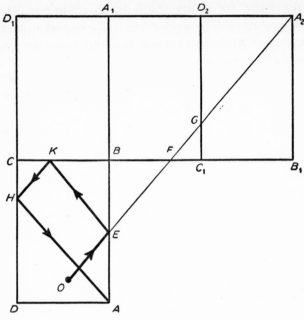

Fig. 19

center, the cue must be aimed toward the imaginary position A_2, as shown in Figure 19.

The Container Problem

One of the oldest problems in mathematical recreations is the problem of containers. Usually, three containers with definite capacity are assumed. The largest is filled with liquid. The player is required to distribute the liquid among the three containers according to predetermined conditions. Let us consider several such problems.

We have three unmarked containers of 12-, 7-, and 5-gallon capacity. The 12-gallon container is full. The problem is to pour into the 7-gallon container 6 gallons of liquid only, and leave 6 gallons in the 12-gallon container.

At the start 12 gallons are in the 12-gallon container. We fill the 5-gallon container, leaving 7 gallons in the 12-gallon container. Next, we empty the 5-gallon container into the 7-gallon container. The succeeding steps are shown in the diagram below. Several other solutions are possible. The arrows indicate the consecutive steps.

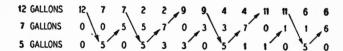

Suppose that we have three containers of 8, 5, and 3 gallons. The 8-gallon container is filled, and we are to put 4 gallons into the 5-gallon container, leaving 4 gallons of liquid in the 8-gallon container. The problem is solved as follows:

In the two problems above, we had 12-, 7-, and 5-gallon containers and 8-, 5-, and 3-gallon containers. In each of these problems the larger container has a capacity equal to the capacity of the remaining two containers, $7 + 5 = 12$ and $5 + 3 = 8$. The following problems show that such a relationship is not required.

A 12-gallon container is filled with liquid. The 9-gallon and 5-gallon containers are empty. The problem is to put 6 gallons of liquid in the 9-gallon container and leave 6 gallons in the 12-gallon container. The problem may be solved as follows:

12 GALLONS	12	7	0	5	5	10	10	1	1	6
9 GALLONS	0	0	7	7	2	2	0	9	6	6
5 GALLONS	0	5	5	0	5	0	2	2	5	0

This problem permits a number of other solutions, all of which may be obtained by experimenting. Even if one does not actually pour liquid from one container to the other, the experiments may be conducted by recording each step. Unfortunately, the solutions given above do not follow any special method; everything is a matter of trial and error. There is, however, a scheme which permits the solutions of such problems.

The Billiard Ball Computer

We shall construct a special billiard table, making use of the properties of the 60° angle. Since there are 180° in a straight angle, an angle of incidence of 60° results in an angle of reflection of 60°, and the angle between the incident and the reflected rays is also 60° (see Figure 20).

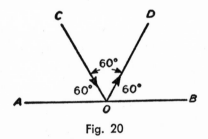

Fig. 20

Let us construct a network (akin to a coordinate system) with the angle between the sides of the network equal to 60° on one side and 120° on the other side of each line. By means of this network we shall develop a system for the solution of the container problems. This system will enable us to:

a. establish the order in which the filling of the various containers is performed,

b. obtain all the possible combinations which may be encountered while such problems are solved, and

c. establish the general procedure for the solution of such problems.

Let us consider the problem of the 12-, 9- and 5-gallon containers. The "billiard table" for this problem is shown in Figure 21. There are nine divisions on the bottom horizontal line. These 9 divisions are assigned to the 9-gallon container. The 5 divisions on the left line are assigned to the 5-gallon container. On the right line 3 divisions are marked off, because $12 - 9 = 3$. It appears as if the parallelogram is cut off at the upper right-hand corner.

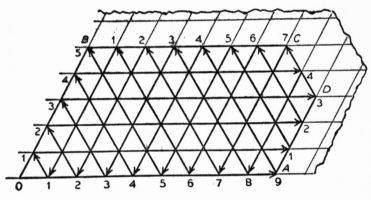

Fig. 21

The principle of operation of this device is based on the properties of the law regarding incidence and reflection as applied to billiard balls. As the billiard ball is sent along the horizontal line OA, it reaches the "cushion" AD, and it is reflected along the line $A4$.

This billiard table has five "cushions," namely, OA, AD, DC, CB, and OB. As soon as the billiard ball reaches a cushion, it immediately determines two associated numbers which must be recorded in a definite order and manner. For example, when the billiard ball reaches the point A, the numbers 9 and 0 must be recorded. The first number is associated with the distance along the horizontal line or cushion, and the second number is associated with the distance along the slanted line, as measured from the horizontal line. Thus, for the point A, the distance along the horizontal line is 9, and the distance along the slanted line for this point is

0 (zero). When the ball, after having been reflected from the point 9 on the "cushion" *AD,* reaches the point 4 on the "cushion" *BC,* its corresponding number is (4,5).

Each such number combination instructs us how to fill the containers. Thus, the combination (9,0) tells us that nine gallons must be poured into the 9-gallon container, while the 5-gallon container must be left empty. When the point 4 on the "cushion" *BC* is reached, we have the combination (4,5). This combination tells us that the 9-gallon container must have 4 gallons of liquid, and 5-gallon container must have 5 gallons of liquid. The operations to be performed should be recorded as follows:

```
12 GALLONS   12   3   3
 9 GALLONS    0   9   4
 5 GALLONS    0   0   5
```

The billiard ball is reflected from the point 4 on the "cushion" *BC* to the point 4 on the "cushion" *OA.* The number combination of this point is (4,0), and means that the 9-gallon container should have 4 gallons of liquid, and 5-gallon container should be emptied. If these instructions are followed, then the contents of the 5-gallon container are returned to the 12-gallon container.

After the reflected billiard ball has left the point 4 on the "cushion" *OA,* it reaches the point 4 on the "cushion" *OB.* The number combination for this point is (0,4). This combination tells us to "Empty the 9-gallon container and put 4 gallons into the 5-gallon container." Our recording up to this moment is:

```
12 GALLONS   12   3   3   8   8
 9 GALLONS    0   9   4   4   0
 5 GALLONS    0   0   5   0   4
```

The next point the reflected billiard ball will reach is on the "cushion" *CD* denoted by the number 4. Its number combination is (8,4) which means that the 8 gallons which are in the 12-gallon container should be poured into the 9-gallon container.

If we continue the procedure described above, the billiard ball will continue to issue instructions, until we reach the solution of our problem. The solution of the problem can be recorded as follows:

This solution is longer than the one we obtained earlier. The billiard ball method may, however, be applied starting along the "cushion" OB. The billiard ball will reach the point B whose number combination is $(0,5)$. From point B the billiard ball must be sent along the "cushion" BC to the point $(7,5)$. From the point 7 on the "cushion" BC the ball will be reflected to point 7 on the "cushion" OA. The number combination for this point is $(7,0)$. The next number combination will be $(2,5)$.

Assembling the instructions which have been given by the billiard ball thus far we have:

12 GALLONS	12	7	0	5	5
9 GALLONS	0	0	7	7	2
5 GALLONS	0	5	5	0	5

The additional instructions which the billiard ball gives complete the solution, and we have:

This is the solution obtained earlier in this chapter.

Figure 21 contains the required solution and information regarding all the possible fillings of the three containers.

That the problem was solved does not indicate that the work of the billiard ball was completed. That work is considered complete when the ball returns to the point of its departure, that is, the point O. The ball's return means that no additional information can be obtained.

The records of all the information which the billiard ball can supply may contain indications that certain combinations of the filling of the vessel are, under the conditions of a given problem, impossible. If certain requirements are set and if the billiard ball returns to the initial point O without yielding the required solution, the required solution is impossible. The ball cannot fail. Nor can it perform miracles.

Consider, for example, the following problem. A 12-gallon container is filled with liquid. Using a 9-gallon and a 7-gallon container, distribute the liquid so that two of the containers have 6 gallons of liquid each.

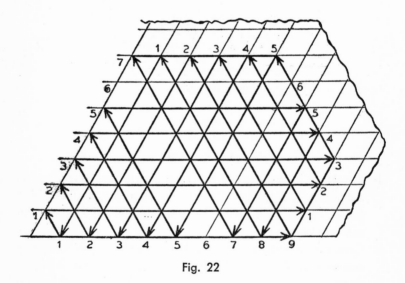

Fig. 22

The billiard ball solution is shown in Figure 22. Note that this diagram does not indicate any number combinations for the positions on the "cushions" which are labeled with the number 6. The tabulation of the instructions given by the billiard ball for all its positions until it has returned to the point O is given below.

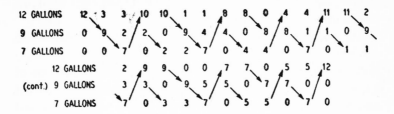

The diagram in Figure 23 represents the information which was provided by the billiard ball for 7-, 5-, and 4-gallon containers when the 7-gallon container is full and the others are empty.

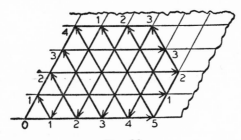

Fig. 23

PROBLEMS

1. Construct a diagram of a billiard table for the following containers: 11-gallon (filled) and 7-gallon and 5-gallon (both empty). Tabulate the information given by the billiard ball.

2. Construct a diagram of a billiard table for the following containers: 7-gallon (filled) and 3-gallon and 5-gallon (both empty). Tabulate the information provided by the billiard ball.

Chapter 3

THE NOTCH
ARITHMETIC

The Twentieth Century Prehistoric Mathematics

We humans are the most conceited of beings. Ask anyone and he will tell you that we are civilized, that we have the most advanced types of machinery, that we have means for traveling faster than sound, that we can transmit pictures with the speed of light (about 186,000 miles a second), that we are about ready to claim real estate on the moon or to subdivide the farmlands on Mars, that we have devised machines which can perform numerical computations faster than any brain and can be said to "think." All this is true or nearly true. But all this is just about one step removed from the mathematical methods discovered by men when they wore no more than animal skins and whose only tools were crudely fashioned clubs. It is a long way from a castle in a cave to an air-conditioned television station, but it is less than a stone's throw from the first steps in counting to the most modern electronic computing machine.

Nowadays we take for granted the fact that we can count and write numbers as large as we please. We have developed a system of writing numbers by means of ten individual digits: 0, 1, 2, 3, 4, 5, 6, 7, 8, and 9. But when counting was discovered the only *digit* that man had was a notch. We still use this notch when we "check off" items on a laundry sheet, when we "take stock" in a warehouse, or when some killer

ation by computing the number of "twos" in the number written in the decimal system of numeration. This computation is performed by means of "long division." Suppose that we have the number 15,683 which is written in the decimal system of numeration. Let us perform the consecutive divisions of this number by 2 as follows:

$$15,683 \div 2 = 7,841 + \text{remainder } 1$$
$$7,841 \div 2 = 3,920 + \text{remainder } 1$$
$$3,920 \div 2 = 1,960 + \text{remainder } 0$$
$$1,960 \div 2 = 980 + \text{remainder } 0$$
$$980 \div 2 = 490 + \text{remainder } 0$$
$$490 \div 2 = 245 + \text{remainder } 0$$
$$245 \div 2 = 122 + \text{remainder } 1$$
$$122 \div 2 = 61 + \text{remainder } 0$$
$$61 \div 2 = 30 + \text{remainder } 1$$
$$30 \div 2 = 15 + \text{remainder } 0$$
$$15 \div 2 = 7 + \text{remainder } 1$$
$$7 \div 2 = 3 + \text{remainder } 1$$
$$3 \div 2 = 1 + \text{remainder } 1$$

The divisions may also be written as:

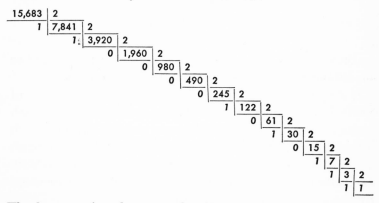

The last quotient becomes the digit on the extreme left of the translation. The number 15,683 in the two-system of numeration is then

$$11,110,101,000,011$$

The translation of 73 into the two-system of numeration is obtained as follows:

```
73 | 2
 1 | 36 | 2
      0 | 18 | 2
           0 | 9 | 2
                1 | 4 | 2
                     0 | 2 | 2
                          0 | 1
```

When 73 is translated into the two-system of numeration, it becomes 1,001,001.

A number which is written in the two-system of numeration may be translated into the ten-system (the decimal system) of numeration, provided we keep in mind that the place values in the two-system are all powers of 2. Thus, the number 1,111,011,111 is translated as follows:

$$(1 \cdot 2^9) + (1 \cdot 2^8) + (1 \cdot 2^7) + (1 \cdot 2^6) + (0 \cdot 2^5)$$
$$+ (1 \cdot 2^4) + (1 \cdot 2^3) + (1 \cdot 2^2) + (1 \cdot 2) + 1$$

or $512 + 256 + 128 + 64 + 16 + 8 + 4 + 2 + 1 = 991$

PROBLEMS

1. Translate 784 into the two-system of numeration.
2. Translate 100,101,001,000,101 into the ten-system of numeration.
3. Translate 16,782,453 into the two-system of numeration.

Some Notch Magic

The two-system of numeration is so versatile that by its application some very interesting tricks may be performed. The applications of this system of numeration to practical problems are also numerous. The writing of coded messages was once based in principle on this system of numeration.*

The two-system of numeration equivalents of a series of ten-system numbers are given in the table on page 29.

* See A. Bakst, *Mathematics, Its Magic and Mastery*, New York: D. Van Nostrand Co., Inc., 1952, pp. 91-98.

Ten-System	Two-System	Ten-System	Two-System	Ten-System	Two-System	Ten-System	Two-System
1	1	26	11,010	51	110,011	76	1,001,100
2	10	27	11,011	52	110,100	77	1,001,101
3	11	28	11,100	53	110,101	78	1,001,110
4	100	29	11,101	54	110,110	79	1,001,111
5	101	30	11,110	55	110,111	80	1,010,000
6	110	31	11,111	56	111,000	81	1,010,001
7	111	32	100,000	57	111,001	82	1,010,010
8	1,000	33	100,001	58	111,010	83	1,010,011
9	1,001	34	100,010	59	111,011	84	1,010,100
10	1,010	35	100,011	60	111,100	85	1,010,101
11	1,011	36	100,100	61	111,101	86	1,010,110
12	1,100	37	100,101	62	111,110	87	1,010,111
13	1,101	38	100,110	63	111,111	88	1,011,000
14	1,110	39	100,111	64	1,000,000	89	1,011,001
15	1,111	40	101,000	65	1,000,001	90	1,011,010
16	10,000	41	101,001	66	1,000,010	91	1,011,011
17	10,001	42	101,010	67	1,000,011	92	1,011,100
18	10,010	43	101,011	68	1,000,100	93	1,011,101
19	10,011	44	101,100	69	1,000,101	94	1,011,110
20	10,100	45	101,101	70	1,000,110	95	1,011,111
21	10,101	46	101,110	71	1,000,111	96	1,100,000
22	10,110	47	101,111	72	1,001,000	97	1,100,001
23	10,111	48	110,000	73	1,001,001	98	1,100,010
24	11,000	49	110,001	74	1,001,010	99	1,100,011
25	11,001	50	110,010	75	1,001,011	100	1,100,100

Using the foregoing table of numbers, we can construct seven tables of numbers.

The first table of numbers (all written in the ten-system of numeration) will consist of numbers whose equivalents in the two-system of numeration have the digit "1" on the extreme right (that is, the equivalents of the numbers 1, 11, 101, 1,011, 100,011, etc.). The second table will contain all the numbers in the ten-system of numeration whose equivalents in the two-system of numeration have the digit "1" in the second place from the right (that is, the equivalents of the numbers 10, 110, 11,010, etc.). In like manner, Tables 3 through 7 will contain all the numbers in the ten-system of numeration whose equivalents in the two-system of numeration have the digit "1" in the third, fourth, fifth, sixth, and seventh places from the right, respectively. The tables follow:

TABLE 1

1	21	41	61	81
3	23	43	63	83
5	25	45	65	85
7	27	47	67	87
9	29	49	69	89
11	31	51	71	91
13	33	53	73	93
15	35	55	75	95
17	37	57	77	97
19	39	59	79	99

TABLE 2

2	22	42	62	82
3	23	43	63	83
6	26	46	66	86
7	27	47	67	87
10	30	50	70	90
11	31	51	71	91
14	34	54	74	94
15	35	55	75	95
18	38	58	78	98
19	39	59	79	99

TABLE 3

4	22	44	62	79
5	23	45	63	84
6	28	46	68	85
7	29	47	69	86
12	30	52	70	87
13	31	53	71	92
14	36	54	76	93
15	37	55	77	94
20	38	60	78	95
21	39	61		100

TABLE 4

8	26	44	62	88
9	27	45	63	89
10	28	46	72	90
11	29	47	73	91
12	30	56	74	92
13	31	57	75	93
14	40	58	76	94
15	41	59	77	95
24	42	60	78	
25	43	61	79	

TABLE 5

16	26	52	62	88
17	27	53	63	89
18	28	54	80	90
19	29	55	81	91
20	30	56	82	92
21	31	57	83	93
22	48	58	84	94
23	49	59	85	95
24	50	60	86	
25	51	61	87	

TABLE 6

32	42	52	62
33	43	53	63
34	44	54	96
35	45	55	97
36	46	56	98
37	47	57	99
38	48	58	100
39	49	59	
40	50	60	
41	51	61	

TABLE 7

64	74	84	94
65	75	85	95
66	76	86	96
67	77	87	97
68	78	88	98
69	79	89	99
70	80	90	100
71	81	91	
72	82	92	
73	83	93	

These tables may be transcribed on cards, one table to a card, and used for the following tricks:

Ask anyone to select any number between 1 and 100. Then ask him to tell you the numbers of the tables in which the selected number appears.

If he chose the number 59, he will say his number appears in Tables 1, 2, 4, 5, and 6. You add the first number in each of the respective tables (in this case—1, 2, 8, 16, and 32), and the sum of these numbers will be the number chosen.

You can tell anyone his age, if that person tells you the numbers of the tables in which his age appears.

If some young lady tells you that her age appears in the Tables 2, 3, and 5, you can tell her that she has seen 22 springs. All you have to do is add the first numbers on each of the cards she names.

To mystify everybody further, you need not even consult the tables. If someone gives you a number of a table in which his selected number appears, raise 2 to the power of that number which is 1 less than the number of the table. For example, if the number of the table is 6, then 2 must be raised to the power 5, and this gives 32. Now you know the first number of Table 6. In similar manner you can determine the first number of any other table and, following the procedure given above, you can tell what the selected number is. Remember, a number raised to the zero power is one, so that the first number of Table 1 will always be one.

The foregoing tables may, of course, be enlarged so that they may contain numbers which are larger than 100. If you enlarge the tables, remember the method used and described of constructing tables above.

The Purse Magic

This trick requires preliminary preparations which must be kept secret from those before whom it is to be performed. Ten purses and six dollars in change are needed. The money should be distributed among the 10 purses as follows:

Purse number 1 (the purses should be numbered consecutively) will contain 1 cent.
Purse number 2 will contain 2 cents.
Purse number 3 will contain 4 cents.
Purse number 4 will contain 8 cents.
Purse number 5 will contain 16 cents.
Purse number 6 will contain 32 cents.
Purse number 7 will contain 64 cents.
Purse number 8 will contain $1.28.
Purse number 9 will contain $2.56.
Purse number 10 will contain 89 cents.

Note that

$$1 + 2 + 4 + 8 + 16 + 32 + 64 + 128 + 256 + 89 = 600$$

After the preliminary arrangements have been completed and the purses have been properly labeled, announce that any amount of money up to and including $6.00 may be obtained without counting. To add even more mystery, you may suggest that you will not touch the purses.

Suppose that someone suggests the sum of $4.37. After some mumbo jumbo (you may use any incantations you choose), ask that the following purses be picked up: 3, 4, 5, 7, 9, and 10. These purses contain the following sums of money:

$$4 + 8 + 16 + 64 + 256 + 89 = 437$$

This trick is based on the properties of the two-system of numeration. When an amount of money is stated, subtract 89 (the amount of money in the tenth purse) from it and translate the difference into the two-system of numeration. When translated into the two-system of numeration, 348 becomes 101, 011,100. The zeros indicate the purses which should not be touched. Working from the right, the purses *not* to be touched are those labeled 1, 2, 6, and 8.

You may also work this trick another way. Instead of subtracting 89 from the given number, you may proceed with the translation of this number into the two-system of numeration immediately. When 437 is translated into the two-system, it is written as 110,110,101. The positions of the digits "1," when read from the right, indicate the numbers of the required purses. Thus,

$$1 + 4 + 16 + 32 + 128 + 256 = 437$$

The purse with the 89 cents is provided for the cases involving the selection of sums exceeding $5.11 because

$$1 + 2 + 4 + 8 + 16 + 32 + 64 + 128 + 256 = 511.$$

If, for example, the sum of $5.72 were selected, it is translated into the two-system of numeration as 1,000,111,100. A purse containing $5.12 would be required. However, if you care to increase the number of purses, and, consequently, increase the amount of change which is to be placed in the purses, you may vary this trick at will.

PROBLEMS

4. Set up a distribution of change so that any amount up to and including $7.50 may be selected.
5. Set up a distribution of change so that any amount up to and including $12.00 may be selected.

Chapter 4

VERSATILITY OF
THE NOTCH
ARITHMETIC

Arithmetic Was Never So Easy

The easiest way to learn arithmetic, as any school child soon finds out, is via hard work. It takes years of drudgery to learn addition, multiplication, subtraction, and division. Learning the multiplication table is sometimes as complicated as mastering the Theory of Relativity. Although teachers used to require that the multiplication table be memorized, modern educators frown on such procedures. After all, memorizing at least 100 separate facts is really a difficult task.

In the case of an arithmetic in which the only symbol employed is the notch, all the arithmetic operations are simple. For example, if we have two notch records, /// ///// ///// ///// ///// ///// and // ///// ///// ///// /////, the addition is performed as follows:

/// ///// ///// ///// ///// /////
$$+ \text{ // ///// ///// ///// /////}$$
$$= \text{///// ///// ///// ///// ///// /////}$$
$$\text{///// ///// ///// /////}$$

Multiplication is performed as follows:

$$(\text{// //////}) \cdot (\text{/// //////}) = (\text{// //////}) + (\text{// //////})$$
$$+ (\text{// //////}) + (\text{// //////}) + (\text{// //////}) + (\text{// //////})$$
$$+ (\text{// //////}) + (\text{// //////}) = \text{/ ///// ///// ///// /////}$$
$$\text{///// ///// ///// ///// ///// ///// /////}$$

34

This same multiplication may be performed according to the column multiplication method as follows:

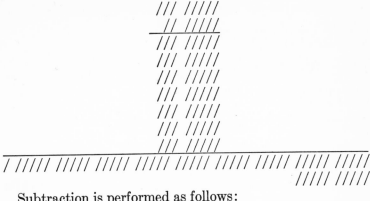

Subtraction is performed as follows:

$$// \ ///// \ ///// \ ///// \ ///// \ /////$$
$$- \ /// \ ///// \ ///// \ ///// \ = \ //// \ /////$$

However, the use of the notch alone for performing arithmetic operations can become very cumbersome.

What Zero Can Accomplish

If in addition to the notch (which for our purposes may be replaced by the symbol "1") we also make use of the symbol "0," we introduce a system of numeration in the arithmetic of the notch. This is the two-system of numeration which was described in Chapter 3. The arithmetic operations of the two-system of numeration are simple. The facts one needs to remember may be condensed into three statements:

$$1 + 1 = 10, \quad 1 \cdot 1 = 1, \quad \text{and} \quad 1 \cdot 0 = 0$$

Addition in the two-system of numeration is performed as follows:

$$\begin{array}{r} 11 \ 010 \ 100 \ 110 \ 011 \\ 1 \ 110 \ 101 \ 011 \ 101 \\ \hline 101 \ 001 \ 010 \ 010 \ 000 \end{array}$$

Since $1 + 1 = 10$, whenever this addition combination occurs we write "0" in that place and "carry" 1 into the next place to the left.

Multiplication in the two-system of numeration is performed as follows:

```
              110 010 100 101 001
                  101 001 111 001
              ───────────────────
              110 010 100 101 001
          110 010 100 101 001
        1 100 101 001 010 01
       11 001 010 010 100 1
      110 010 100 101 001
  110 010 100 101 001
 11 001 010 010 100 1
 ──────────────────────────────
100 001 000 110 110 101 001 100 001
```

Subtraction in the two-system is performed as follows:

```
 ··  ·   ·   ···  ·
11 011 001 100 000 111
 1 110 010 011 110 101
 ─────────────────────
 1 100 111 000 010 010
```

The "dots" above the numerals indicate "borrowing," a procedure which is also employed in the arithmetic of the decimal system.

Division in the two-system of numeration is performed as follows:

```
11 100 111 010 101    │1001
10 01                  11001101101
──────
 1 010
 1 001
 ──────
    1 111
    1 001
    ──────
      110 0
      100 1
      ──────
        1 110
        1 001
        ──────
          101 1
          100 1
          ──────
            1 001
```

The quotient is 110 101 000, and the remainder 101.

The division may be carried on, and this will yield a

decimal (in the sense of the two-system of numeration) fraction. Thus, we have

$$
\begin{array}{r|l}
101 & 1001 \\
\underline{1001} & 0.1000111 \\
10001 & \\
\underline{1001} & \\
10000 & \\
\underline{1001} & \\
1110 & \\
\underline{1001} & \\
101 & \\
\end{array}
$$

The sequence of digits 101 indicates that we have a repeating fraction (we will call the fractions in the two-system of numeration *two-mals*).

$$0.1000111 \ 1000111 \ 1000111 \ldots$$

The two-mal fraction 0.1 is equivalent to $\frac{1}{2}$ in the decimal system of numeration. The two-mal fraction 0.01 is equivalent to $\frac{1}{4}$, and the two-mal fraction 0.001 is equivalent to $\frac{1}{8}$ in the decimal system of numeration. Each and every position to the right is equal in value to one half of the value of the place to its left, whether these positions are indicated by a "two-mal point" or otherwise.

The "two-mal fraction" 0.1000111 has the value of

$$\tfrac{1}{2} + \tfrac{1}{32} + \tfrac{1}{64} + \tfrac{1}{128} = \tfrac{71}{128}$$

The fraction $\frac{101}{1001}$ has the value of $\frac{5}{9}$ which is larger than the value of 0.1000111 by $\frac{1}{1152}$.

How the Giant Brain Works

Modern electronic computers perform arithmetic operations as well as other mathematical computations and calculations with speeds which stagger the imagination. Problems that would require hundreds of hours and scores of mathematicians and computers may be solved by the electronic computing devices in minutes or seconds.

There are two kinds of devices. The first type is designed to solve specific problems. These machines have special components which resemble specific mathematical expressions or formulas. Their principle of construction resembles that of the slide rule, although they do not have the appearance of slide rules. These devices are known as *analog computers* because there is an analogy between their construction and the mathematical structure of the problems which they are designed to solve.

The other type of computer represents a more general construction and resembles a computing device in which the component parts correspond to the symbols for numbers. These electronic computing devices are known as *digital computers*. A digital computer will perform the arithmetic operations of addition, subtraction, multiplication, division in much the way a cash register or an adding machine operates. In place of mechanical moving parts, however, an electronic digital computer consists of series of vacuum tubes similar to those which may be found in a radio receiver, although specially designed for the purposes of the computer.

There is a variety of digital electronic computers now in operation and new ones are being constructed and planned. Some are so complex in structure that years are required to put them together. Today, an electronic computer which contains several thousand vacuum tubes is considered very simple. Some digital electronic computers contain tubes which act as though they were endowed with memory, for they can store away thousands of numbers, each consisting of many digits.

In principle, however, the operation of an electronic digital computer is very simple. The basis of all operations performed by these computers is the two-system or binary-system of numeration, although more advanced devices rely on other systems of numeration. The electronic digital computer which is based on the two-system of numeration is known as the binary electronic digital computer.

Because there are only two digits in the "two-system" of numeration, the problem of recording these digits by means of a vacuum tube resolves into a simple procedure of "opening" and "closing" an electric circuit. When the circuit is *open,* or current is not passing, it may be considered as representing the digit "0"; a *closed* circuit may be considered as the representation of the digit "1." Relays and other techniques are necessary if the correct results are to be obtained.

The reader who wishes to obtain detailed information concerning electronic computing devices may consult the following books:

Edmund C. Berkeley, *Giant Brains or Machines That Think.* John Wiley and Sons, Inc., New York, 1949.
Engineering Research Associates, Inc., *High Speed Computing Devices.* McGraw-Hill Book Company, Inc., New York, 1950.

Electronic computing devices operate from "instructions" which are prepared in advance and placed on tapes, often by means of punched holes. Before a binary electronic computing device can be put to work, all numbers in the decimal system of numeration must be translated into the "two-system"; however, the more advanced electronic computing devices provide for automatic translation.

Writing numbers in the two-system results in very large combinations of the digits "0" and "1." For example, the number 18,926, when translated becomes 101,000,000,110,010. Thus, the "recording" of the number 18,926 on a binary electronic computing device requires fifteen vacuum tubes.

The internal design of a computer must provide for special relays to take care of all the arithmetic processes so that all operations are performed automatically and the results are stated as they appear on additional vacuum tubes. Thus, for example, the following addition when it is performed on a binary electronic computing device depends entirely on the correct arrangement of relays:

$$\begin{array}{r} 1001101 \\ \underline{110110} \\ 10000011 \end{array}$$

These relays automatically close and open the circuits in accordance with the rules for addition in the two-system of numeration.

Eight Comes to the Rescue

The writing of numbers in the two-system of numeration becomes very cumbersome. However, this writing may be simplified. The simplification is introduced into the construction of the binary electronic computing devices so that the recording and the typing of the final numerical results become comparatively simple. Note the following combinations of the digits "0" and "1" in the two-system of numeration:

000	represents	0	100 represents 4
001	represents	1	101 represents 5
010	represents	2	110 represents 6
011	represents	3	111 represents 7

These triplets may be employed in translating numbers written in the two-system of numeration. By translating the triplets according to the scheme above,

11,001,010,000,101,110,100,011,100,111,101,001

becomes

312,056,434,751

The number 312,056,434,751 is, however, not written in the decimal system of numeration. That only the digits 0, 1, 2, 3, 4, 5, 6, and 7 are used suggests that this number is written in the eight-system of numeration. In the eight-system of numeration (which is also known as the *octal* system) the digit "7" plays the same role as the digit "9" in the decimal system of numeration.

The advantage of the octal system over the two-system of numeration lies in the fact that in the octal system fewer digits are required for writing numbers. The translation of a number written in the octal system of numeration into the two-system of numeration can be performed with almost no effort. Electronic computing devices make provisions for such translations automatically. Thus, for example, the number 15,675,217,346,320,016,536 when written in the octal system of numeration is translated into

1,101,110,111,101,010,001,111,011,100,110,011,010,-
000,000,001,110,101,011,110

The translation of a number written in the octal system of numeration into a number written in the decimal system of numeration will be explained in Chapter 5.

PROBLEMS

1. Add 101,011,110,111 and 10,000,110,011.
2. Add 111,111,000,111,001,011,111 and 101,010,101,-
   010,101.
3. Subtract 11,000,111,101,111,011 from 100,101,001,-
   000,100,101,001.
4. Subtract 11,111,111,111,111,111,111,111 from 110,000,-
   000,000,111,001,111,000,001.
5. Multiply 11,111,111,111,111,111 by 111,111,111,111,-
   001.
6. Multiply 101,010,101,010,101 by 11,111,000,111,000.
7. Divide 111,000,111,000,111,000 by 10,101,010,101.
   Carry the division four places beyond the two-mal point.
8. Divide 10,100,100,000,010,011,111 by 11,111,111,111.
   Carry the division four places beyond the two-mal point.
9. Translate 11,110,101,011,111,010,000,100,010,011,-
   010,101,110,000,001,011 into the octal system of numeration.

10. Translate 111,101,010,000,011,101,111,101,010,011,-001,111,110,100 into the octal system of numeration.
11. Translate the octal number, 157,634,527,100,735,612, into the two-system of numeration.
12. Translate the octal number, 700,052,104,265,724,315,-273,341,261,514, into the two-system of numeration.

Chapter 5

FANCY AND ASSORTED COUNTING SYSTEMS

The Oldest Multiplication Method

The method of multiplication to be described dispenses with the multiplication table. Although the origin of this method is lost in antiquity, almost every nation claims it. In Eastern Europe it goes under the name of the "Russian Peasants' Multiplication." There is sufficient evidence, however, to establish that the method was known to the Ancient Egyptians about 2,000 years B.C.

The principle of the method is very simple. Suppose two numbers are to be multiplied. If one number is halved, and the other is doubled and these two multiplied, the product will be the same as that of the original numbers. This halving and doubling may be carried on until the halving reaches finally a quotient of "1." At this point, the multiplication is completed.

For example, the product of 32 and 15 is obtained as follows:

Halving	Doubling
32	15
16	30
8	60
4	120
2	240
1	480

Thus $32 \cdot 15 = 480$.

Unfortunately, the example does not provide the general rule. The reader will observe that the number that was halved was 32, and all the resulting halves are even numbers.

Let us consider the case in which the number to be halved is even or odd, and the resulting halves are either even or odd. Perform the multiplication $53 \cdot 39$.

The number 53 (which is written in the decimal system of numeration) is translated into the two-system numeration as 110,101. In other words,

$$53 = (1 \cdot 2^5) + (1 \cdot 2^4) + (1 \cdot 2^2) + 1$$

The product $53 \cdot 39$ may be written as

$$[(1 \cdot 2^5) + (1 \cdot 2^4) + (1 \cdot 2^2) + 1)] \cdot 39,$$

or as the sum

$$39 + (39 \cdot 2^2) + (39 \cdot 2^4) + (39 \cdot 2^5)$$

The halving and doubling scheme as shown in the case of the product of 32 and 15, when applied to the product of 53 and 39, appears as follows:

Halving	Doubling	Summing
53	39	39
26	78	....
13	156	156
6	312	....
3	624	624
1	1248	1248
		2067

The rule for halving and doubling and finally summing may then be stated:

Whenever the multiplicand to be halved is odd, take the multiplicand as an addend. If the first multiplicand is even, disregard its corresponding multiplicand and continue the halving and doubling until an odd number is reached. When the column with the multiplicands that are halved reaches "one", that is "1", the process of halving and doubling is completed. Then add the recorded addends, and the sum thus obtained is the required product.

The rule applies to all the possible cases of multiplication. The product of 32 and 15 is no exception to this rule. The reader will note that all the consecutive halves obtained from 32 are even, except the last which is "1" and, thus, the only addend to be used is 480. The product of 32 and 15 is therefore 480.

Observe that, whenever an odd number is halved, and a remainder "1" is obtained, this remainder is to be discarded. But this remainder is "put to use" by multiplying by it the doubled number which corresponds to the halved, and this product is used as an addend. For example,

Halving	Remainder	Doubling	Summing
27	1	34	34
13	1	68	68
6	0	136	...
3	1	272	272
1	1	544	544
			918

PROBLEMS

1. Obtain the product of 72 and 57. Check the result by halving 57 and doubling 72.
2. Obtain the product of 16 and 128. Check the result by halving 128 and doubling 16.
3. Obtain the product of 87 and 95. Check the result by halving 95 and doubling 87.

Weighing Economy

Businesses selling goods that must be weighed are usually equipped nowadays with scales which do not require weights. However, there are some which still use the old-fashioned weighing instruments that employ the principle of balance. Such instruments have two platforms. The object to be weighed is put on one platform and a weight (or combination of weights) is put on the other so that the two platforms balance. Although one could use weights corresponding to the series of numbers from one on to any desired number, it would be uneconomical to have weights of every denomination. The problem of the selection of weights may be solved, however, quite satisfactorily by considering the properties of the two-system of numeration. Two-system numbers represent the sums of powers of 2. If weights which represent the powers of 2 are selected, a great many combinations are possible.

If we start out with single weights of 1, 2, 4, 8, 16, and 32 pounds, we may obtain weights up to and including 63 pounds. For example, the combination of 1-, 4-, 8-, and 32-pound weights provides 45 pounds. In the "two-system" of numeration 45 is represented by 101101. In terms of the weights to be used, 101101 simply means, reading from right to left, one weight each marked 1-pound, 4-pound (2^2), 8-pound (2^3), and 32-pound (2^5).

If we wish to obtain weights up to and including 127 pounds a 64-pound weight will have to be added. To obtain weights up to and including 255 pounds, a 128-pound weight must be added. Thus, in order to be able to weigh objects up to and including 255 pounds (all the weights expressed in integral pounds), we require only 7 single weights.

Suppose that we want to set up a method for weighing objects up to and including 40 pounds, but we are restricted to 4 different weights. The two-system of numeration is powerless in the case of such restrictions, but the problem has a solution. The four weights are 1, 3, 9, and 27 pounds.

The various weights from 1 to 40 pounds (in integral pounds), as they are obtained with the four weights, are shown in the table.

Weight	Left Side of Balance	Right Side of Balance	Weight	Left Side of Balance	Right Side of Balance
1	1	0	21	27 + 3	9
2	3	1	22	27 + 3 + 1	9
3	3	0	23	27	3 + 1
4	3 + 1	0	24	27	3
5	9	3 + 1	25	27 + 1	3
6	9	3	26	27	1
7	9 + 1	3	27	27	0
8	9	1	28	27 + 1	0
9	9	0	29	27 + 3	1
10	9 + 1	0	30	27 + 3	0
11	9 + 3	1	31	27 + 3 + 1	0
12	9 + 3	0	32	27 + 9	3 + 1
13	9 + 3 + 1	0	33	27 + 9	3
14	27	9 + 3 + 1	34	27 + 9 + 1	3
15	27	9 + 3	35	27 + 9	1
16	27 + 1	9 + 3	36	27 + 9	0
17	27	9 + 1	37	27 + 9 + 1	0
18	27	9	38	27 + 9 + 3	1
19	27 + 1	9	39	27 + 9 + 3	0
20	27 + 3	9 + 1	40	27 + 9 + 3 + 1	0

The symbol "0" in the table indicates that no weight is placed on one side of the balance scale.

Were we to add another weight of 81 pounds, all integral weights from 1 to 121 pounds inclusive could be obtained.

PROBLEMS

4. Write a table of weights from 1 to 40 pounds inclusive if four 1-pound and four 9-pound weights are used.

5. Write a table of weights from 1 to 40 pounds inclusive if one 1-pound, one 3-pound, and four 9-pound weights are used.

6. Write a table of weights from 1 to 40 pounds inclusive if one 1-pound, four 3-pound, and one 27-pound weights are used.

7. Write a table of weights from 1 to 40 pounds inclusive if four 1-pound, one 9-pound, and one 27-pound weights are used.

One Step from the Notch and a New Arithmetic

The solution of the problem of the four weights with which it becomes possible to weigh up to and including 40 pounds (in whole pounds) is closely associated with the system of numeration whose base is 3. The clue to this fact could have been detected when the 1-, 3-, 9-, and 27-pound weights were selected. Note that these four numbers may be represented as powers of 3 as follows: 1, 3, 3^2, and 3^3.

In the three-system of numeration there are only three digits, namely, "0," "1," and "2." The digit "2" in the three-system of numeration plays the role that is assigned to the digit "9" in the decimal system. In the three-system of numeration the place values are multiplied by three as we move from the right to the left. Recall that in the two-system these place values are doubled, while in the decimal system the place values are multiplied by 10.

Since in the three-system of numeration there are only three digits, the number "3" plays the same role as the number "10" plays in the decimal system of numeration. Thus, in the three-system of numeration the number 3 is represented by "10." The counting in the three-system of numeration is carried out as follows: 1, 2, 10, 11, 12, 20, and so on. The relations between the numbers in the decimal system of numeration and the three-system of numeration are shown in the table.

Decimal Numbers	Three-System Numbers	Decimal Numbers	Three-System Numbers	Decimal Numbers	Three-System Numbers
1	1	11	102	21	210
2	2	12	110	22	211
3	10	13	111	23	212
4	11	14	112	24	220
5	12	15	120	25	221
6	20	16	121	26	222
7	21	17	122	27	1000
8	22	18	200	28	1001
9	100	19	201	29	1002
10	101	20	202	30	1010

The translation of numbers written in the decimal system of numeration into numbers in the three-system of numeration is performed by means of long division in a manner analogous to the procedure employed in the translation of decimal numbers into the two-system of numeration. For example, the decimal number 683 is translated as follows:

```
683 |3
681  227 |3
  2  225  75 |3
       2   75  25 |3
            0  24   8 |3
                1   6   2
                    2
```

The number in the three-system of numeration corresponding to the decimal number 683 is 221,022.

The translation of a number written in the three-system of numeration into a number written in the decimal system of numeration is performed as follows. Suppose that the number is 1,022,012. We have then (remembering that the base is 3)

$$(1 \cdot 3^6) + (2 \cdot 3^4) + (2 \cdot 3^3) + (1 \cdot 3) + 2$$

equal to

$$(1 \cdot 729) + (2 \cdot 81) + (2 \cdot 27) + 3 + 2$$
$$= 729 + 162 + 54 + 3 + 2$$

Performing the final addition, we obtain the decimal number 950.

PROBLEMS

8. Translate the following decimal numbers into numbers written in the three-system of numeration. (a) 1,894; (b) 20,471; (c) 100,142.

9. Translate the following three-system numbers into decimal numbers. (a) 120,110; (b) 1,111,111; (c) 21,212,121.

Counting in Other Systems Is Simple

The general principle of counting in a given system of numeration is comparatively simple. Whenever a base is selected and a number is assigned to that base, the number of permissible digits is controlled by that number. If the base is 10, we are allowed ten digits. If the base is 2, we are allowed two digits; if the base is 100, we would be allowed one hundred digits. It should be understood and kept in mind that "zero" (0) is a digit.

The names for the first ten digits, that is, for 0, 1, 2, 3, 4, 5, 6, 7, 8, and 9 may be used for systems of numeration with bases up to 10. If the bases of the system of numeration are greater than 10, however, special names will have to be devised for the additional digits. For example, if the system of numeration has the base 12, it will have twelve digits: 0, 1, 2, 3, 4, 5, 6, 7, 8, 9, t, and e. The symbol t represents the digit "ten." The symbol e represents the digit "eleven." *
In the twelve-system of numeration, the number "10" is read "twelve."

In the five-system of numeration, we count as follows:

1	one	11	five-one	21	two-five-one	31	three-five-one
2	two	12	five-two	22	two-five-two	32	three-five-two
3	three	13	five-three	23	two-five-three	33	three-five-three
4	four	14	five-four	24	two-five-four	34	three-five-four
10	five	20	two-five	30	three-five	40	four-five

41	four-five-one	101	five-five-one	111	five-five-one-five-one
42	four-five-two	102	five-five-two	112	five-five-one-five-two
43	four-five-three	103	five-five-three	113	five-five-one-five-three
44	four-five-four	104	five-five-four	114	five-five-one-five-four
100	five-five	110	five-five-one-five	120	five-five-two-five

If the terms "one-five," "two-five," "five-five," "five-five-one-five" do not suit the reader, he may invent his own set of names and terms.

---

* A detailed examination of systems of numeration with bases up and including 12 may be found in the book by Aaron Bakst, *Mathematics, Its Magic and Mastery*, 2nd edition, D. Van Nostrand Co., Inc., New York, 1952, pp. 9-30, 33, 34.

PROBLEM

10. Count in the six-system and write the numbers up to and inclusive of six-six-one-six.

Number Systems Are Related to One Another

The counting in different number systems may be related to some "primary" number systems, such as the two-system, three-system, and so on. The general principle of this relation is governed by the properties of the number that is the base of a given number system which, in turn, may be ascertained in terms of the factors of the numbers representing the various bases. For example, the four-system of numeration has the base 4. The factors of 4 are 2 and 2 (we disregard the factor 1). Thus, the four-system of numeration is related to the two-system of numeration. If we write the first four numbers in the "two-system" of numeration, we have:

00	represents 0	10	represents 2
01	represents 1	11	represents 3

Then, if we have some number written in the two-system of numeration, say,

$$11011001010110$$

we rewrite it, pairing off the digits from right to left, and get

$$11,01,10,01,01,01,10$$

Now, employing the stated relationship, we rewrite this number as

$$3121112$$

in the four-system of numeration. If these two numbers were translated into the decimal system, the results would be equal:

$$2^{13} + 2^{12} + 2^{10} + 2^9 + 2^6 + 2^4 + 2^2 + 2 = 13,910$$
$$(3 \cdot 4^6) + (4^5) + (2 \cdot 4^4) + (4^3) + (4^2) + (4) + (2) = 13,910$$

If we have a number which is written in the four-system of numeration, then it can be quickly translated into the two-system of numeration. For example, suppose that the number (written in the four-system of numeration) is

230110301211021

The four relations discussed above enable us to translate this number into the two-system of numeration. We have then

1011000101001100011001010001001

PROBLEMS

11. Translate the two-system number

11010001011110101101110001010011001

into the four-system.

12. Translate the four-system number

3022101103321010200332101

into the two-system.

If we write the first eight numbers in the two-system of numeration we have:

000	represents	0	100	represents	4
001	represents	1	101	represents	5
010	represents	2	110	represents	6
011	represents	3	111	represents	7

If a number is written in the two-system of numeration, as, for example,

100111110010101011001

it can be rewritten so that the digits are arranged in triplets as follows:

100,111,110,010,101,011,001

Then, each of the triplets may be translated according to

the relationships stated above. We have then

$$4,762,531$$

This number is written in the eight-system of numeration. The reader will note that the relations of the triplets given above provide for eight digits only, namely, for 0, 1, 2, 3, 4, 5, 6, and 7. The eight-system of numeration requires only eight digits.

If we have a number which is written in the eight-system of numeration, then, by means of the relations of the triplets given above, this number can be translated into the two-system of numeration. Thus, for example, the following number

$$67,132,547,261,773$$

is written in the eight-system of numeration. When translated into the two-system of numeration it is

$$110,111,001,011,010,101,100,111,010,110,001,111,111,011$$

PROBLEMS

13. Translate the two-system number

$$11,010,101,011,000,101,111,110,010,101$$

into the eight-system of numeration.
14. Translate the eight-system number

$$143,746,667,104,770,135,527,701,177$$

into the two-system.

Counting to Three and to Nine

If we have only three digits, namely, 0, 1, and 2, then the system of numeration which is based on that many digits is known as the three-system of numeration. In such a system the digit "2" plays the same role as the digit "9" plays in the decimal system of numeration. In order to translate a decimal number into the three-system of numeration we

employ the process of division by three as shown below. The
decimal number 48298 is translated into the three-system
as follows:

```
48298 |3
48297  16099 |3
    1  16098  5366 |3
        1  5364  1788 |3
            2  1788  596 |3
                0  594  198 |3
                    2  198  66 |3
                        0  66  22 |3
                            0  21  7 |3
                                1  6  2
                                   1
```

The number translated into the three-system of numeration is then

$$2,110,020,211$$

The translation of a number which is written in the three-
system into an equivalent number in the decimal system
follows the same scheme as that used in other systems of
numeration. Thus, for example, the number 102,121, written
in the three-system of numeration, is translated into the
decimal system as follows:

$$(1 \cdot 3^5) + (2 \cdot 3^3) + (1 \cdot 3^2) + (2 \cdot 3) + 1$$
$$= 243 + 54 + 9 + 6 + 1 = 313$$

PROBLEMS

15. Translate the decimal number 89,735,318,239 into the
three-system.
16. Translate the three-system number 10,202,112 into the
decimal system.

If we write the first nine numbers in the three-system of
numeration we have:

00	represents	0	11 represents 4
01	represents	1	12 represents 5
02	represents	2	20 represents 6
10	represents	3	21 represents 7

22   represents   8

If a number is written in the three-system of numeration, as, for example,

210220101120201210002211012212

it can be rewritten so that all the digits are arranged in pairs, as follows:

21,02,20,10,11,20,20,12,10,00,22,11,01,22,12

Then, each of the pairs may be translated according to the relationship stated above. We have then

726,346,653,084,185

This number is written in the nine-system of numeration. The reader will observe that the relations of the pairs given above provide for nine digits only, namely, 0, 1, 2, 3, 4, 5, 6, 7, and 8. The nine-system of numeration requires only nine digits. In the nine-system of numeration the digit "8" plays the same role which is played by the digit "9" in the decimal system of numeration.

If we have a number which is written in the nine-system of numeration, then, by means of the relation of the pairs given above, this number can be translated into the three-system of numeration. Thus, for example, the following number

473,481,023,118,746,218

is written in the nine-system of numeration. When translated into the three-system of numeration (by means of the above relations of the pairs) it is

112,110,112,201,000,210,010,122,211,120,020,122

PROBLEMS

17. Translate the three-system number

102,202,122,111,001,212,110,211

into the nine-system of numeration.

18. Translate the nine-system number

811,002,253,768,702,182,003,440,124

into the three-system of numeration.

Chapter 6

MATHEMATICAL
HANDS ACROSS
THE SEA

How the Romans Counted

For many centuries, before the numbers which are presently employed throughout almost the entire world had been introduced, people made use of a system of counting which was originally employed in the Roman Empire. Even today, the symbols know as "Roman Numerals" quite often appear on the faces of clocks and watches.

Those who complain that the arithmetic of the present time is difficult should take comfort in the fact that we have dispensed with the Roman Numerals. We do not know whether the Roman schoolboy was ever taught to perform arithmetic operations by writing numbers, but it is generally believed that all arithmetic operations were performed on a computing device called an *abacus*. The word *calculate* is derived from the Latin word *calculus* which means *pebble* or *small stone*. The abacus was a small board with grooves in which the pebbles (or *calculi*) were placed. The value of each groove was determined in advance. Thus, a Roman schoolboy, instead of carrying with him some pencils and paper, or a slate and chalk, lugged to school a grooved table and a lot of small stones.

The writing of numbers according to the Romans (and we employ here the ancient style of this writing which did not use the subtractive method) is shown below. The Roman numbers are shown alongside their values in the decimal system of numeration.

Roman	Decimal	Roman	Decimal	Roman	Decimal
	0	XXX........ 30		LX........ 60	
I........ 1		XXXI........ 31		LXI........ 61	
II........ 2		XXXII........ 32		LXII........ 62	
III........ 3		XXXIII........ 33		LXIII........ 63	
IIII........ 4		XXXIIII........ 34		LXIIII........ 64	
V........ 5		XXXV........ 35		LXV........ 65	
VI........ 6		XXXVI........ 36		LXVI........ 66	
VII........ 7		XXXVII........ 37		LXVII........ 67	
VIII........ 8		XXXVIII........ 38		LXVIII........ 68	
VIIII........ 9		XXXVIIII........ 39		LXVIIII........ 69	
X........ 10		XXXX........ 40		LXX........ 70	
XI........ 11		XXXXI........ 41		LXXI........ 71	
XII........ 12		XXXXII........ 42		LXXII........ 72	
XIII........ 13		XXXXIII........ 43		LXXIII........ 73	
XIIII........ 14		XXXXIIII........ 44		LXXIIII........ 74	
XV........ 15		XXXXV........ 45		LXXV........ 75	
XVI........ 16		XXXXVI........ 46		LXXVI........ 76	
XVII........ 17		XXXXVII........ 46		LXXVII........ 77	
XVIII........ 18		XXXXVIII........ 48		LXXVIII........ 78	
XVIIII........ 19		XXXXVIIII........ 49		LXXVIIII........ 79	
XX........ 20		L........ 50		LXXX........ 80	
XXI........ 21		LI........ 51		LXXXI........ 81	
XXII........ 22		LII........ 52		LXXXII........ 82	
XXIII........ 23		LIII........ 53		LXXXIII........ 83	
XXIIII........ 24		LIIII........ 54		LXXXIIII........ 84	
XXV........ 25		LV........ 55		LXXXV........ 85	
XXVI........ 26		LVI........ 56		LXXXVI........ 86	
XXVII........ 27		LVII........ 57		LXXXVII........ 87	
XXVIII........ 28		LVIII........ 58		LXXXVIII........ 88	
XXVIIII........ 29		LVIIII........ 59		LXXXVIIII........ 89	

Roman	Decimal
LXXXX........ 90	
LXXXXI........ 91	
LXXXXII........ 92	
LXXXXIII........ 93	
LXXXXIIII........ 94	
LXXXXV........ 95	
LXXXXVI........ 96	
LXXXXVII........ 97	
LXXXXVIII........ 98	
LXXXXVIIII........ 99	

C........100

Even the Romans Had a System

A cursory examination of Roman numerals reveals some very interesting facts. The basic numerals employed in the Roman system are:

I for 1   V for 5   X for 10   L for 50   C for 100

D for 500   M for 1,000

The numerals I, X, C, and M are repeated as often as four times to indicate several units of the same denomination. Thus 3 is written as III, 40 as XXXX, 400 as CCCC, 3,000 as MMM. The numerals V, L and D are never repeated, since VV is equivalent to X, LL is equivalent to C, and DD is equivalent to M. In the Roman system of numeration the numeral which corresponds to the number "0" is absent.

All this suggests that the Roman system of numeration is some sort of an hybrid system. I, X, C, and M follow the system of numeration which reminds us of the five-system of numeration. V, L, and D follow the two-system of numeration. Thus, the Roman system of numeration may be called the two-five system of numeration, or it may be given a more impressive name employing Latin words, the *bi-quinary* system of numeration.

The table below indicates how the numbers which are written in the Roman system of numeration can be "translated" into the bi-quinary system so that their original properties are preserved. The bi-quinary *place values* are similar to those in any other system of numeration except that every place value is associated with two digits. This is indicated by the commas. By an unwritten agreement the commas are used to separate place values and simplify reading of numbers in the decimal system appear every third number from the right.

Roman	Bi-quinary	Decimal	Roman	Bi-quinary	Decimal
	0	0	L........	10,00	50
I........	1	1	LI........	10,01	51
II........	2	2	LII........	10,02	52
III........	3	3	LIII........	10,03	53
IIII........	4	4	LIIII........	10,04	54
V........	10	5	LV........	10,10	55
VI........	11	6	LVI........	10,11	56
VII........	12	7	LVII........	10,12	57
VIII........	13	8	LVIII........	10,13	58
VIIII........	14	9	LVIIII........	10,14	59
X........	1,00	10	LX........	11,00	60
XI........	1,01	11	LXI........	11,01	61
XII........	1,02	12	LXII........	11,02	62
XIII........	1,03	13	LXIII........	11,03	63
XIIII........	1,04	14	LXIIII........	11,04	64
XV........	1,10	15	LXV........	11,10	65
XVI........	1,11	16	LXVI........	11,11	66
XVII........	1,12	17	LXVII........	11,12	67
XVIII........	1,13	18	LXVIII........	11,13	68
XVIIII........	1,14	19	LXVIIII........	11,14	69
XX........	2,00	20	LXX........	12,00	70
XXI........	2,01	21	LXXI........	12,01	71
XXII........	2,02	22	LXXII........	12,02	72
XXIII........	2,03	23	LXXIII........	12,03	73
XXIIII........	2,04	24	LXXIIII........	12,04	74
XXV........	2,10	25	LXXV........	12,10	75
XXVI........	2,11	26	LXXVI........	12,11	76
XXVII........	2,12	27	LXXVII........	12,12	77
XXVIII........	2,13	28	LXXVIII........	12,13	78
XXVIIII........	2,14	29	LXXVIIII........	12,14	79
XXX........	3,00	30	LXXX........	13,00	80
XXXI........	3,01	31	LXXXI........	13,01	81
XXXII........	3,02	32	LXXXII........	13,02	82
XXXIII........	3,03	33	LXXXIII........	13,03	83
XXXIIII........	3,04	34	LXXXIIII........	13,04	84
XXXV........	3,10	35	LXXXV........	13,10	85
XXXVI........	3,11	36	LXXXVI........	13,11	86
XXXVII........	3,12	37	LXXXVII........	13,12	87
XXXVIII........	3,13	38	LXXXVIII........	13,13	88
XXXVIIII........	3,14	39	LXXXVIIII........	13,14	89
XXXX........	4,00	40	LXXXX........	14,00	90
XXXXI........	4,01	41	LXXXXI........	14,01	91
XXXXII........	4,02	42	LXXXXII........	14,02	92
XXXXIII........	4,03	43	LXXXXIII........	14,03	93
XXXXiiii........	4,04	44	LXXXXIIII........	14,04	94
XXXXV........	4,10	45	LXXXXV........	14,10	95
XXXXVI........	4,11	46	LXXXXVI........	14,11	96
XXXXVII........	4,12	47	LXXXXVII........	14,12	97
XXXXVIII........	4,13	48	LXXXXVIII........	14,13	98
XXXXVIIII........	4,14	49	LXXXXVIIII........	14,14	99
			C........	1,00,00	100

How the Roman Arithmetic Worked

There is no evidence that the Romans employed the method to be described here. The method, however, is a direct consequence of the properties of the bi-quinary system of numeration, and the rules which govern it are similar to the rules of decimal-system arithmetic. These rules are now employed in those electronic computers which are based on the bi-quinary system.

Each bi-quinary place value has two *sub-values.* The digits (0, 1, 2, 3, and 4) which are written on the right side of the place value follow the scheme of the five-system of numeration. The digits (0 and 1) which are written on the left side of the place value follow the scheme of the two- or binary-system of numeration.

The actual numerical operations and their performances become simple when one understands this combination of numeration systems.

To add the bi-quinary numbers 1,13,14 and 10,14,12, we proceed as follows:

2 plus 4, in the five-system of numeration, is 11. We write 1 and "carry" 1.

1 plus 1 plus 1, in the two-system of numeration, is 11. We write 1 and "carry" 1.

1 plus 3 plus 4, in the five-system of numeration, is 13. We write 3 and "carry" 1.

1 plus 1 plus 1, in the two-system of numeration, is 11. We write 1 and "carry" 1.

1 plus 1 plus 0, in the five-system of numeration, is 2. We write 2. There is nothing to "carry."

Finally, we write 1. The sum is 12,13,11.

The operations involved in subtracting bi-quinary numbers can be illustrated if we subtract 2,14,13,11 from 14,03,-12,04 as follows:

4 minus 1 is 3. We write 3.

We borrow 1 from 2. This is then "2" in the two-system of numeration. 2 minus 1 is 1. We write 1.

3 cannot be subtracted from 1. Remember that we borrowed 1 from 2. We borrow 1 from 1 which gives us "5." Then we subtract 3 and 6 and write 3.

We cannot subtract 1 from 0. We borrow 1 from 3, subtract 1 from 2, and write 1.

We cannot subtract 4 from 2. We borrow 1 from 4 to give us 2 where the "0" is. We borrow 1 from 2. Then, together with the 2 (which remained after we borrowed from 3) we have 7. Subtracting 4, we have 3.

1 subtracted from 1 is 0.

2 subtracted from 3 leaves 1.

Finally, we write 1.

The difference is 11,03,13,13. The correctness of the subtraction can be checked by the addition: 11,03,13,13 + 2,14,13,11.

The steps required to multiply bi-quinary numbers are illustrated in the problem $(2,14 \cdot 12)$ below:

The product $2 \cdot 4$ is 8. Write 3 and "carry" 1.

The product $2 \cdot 10$ is 1,00. Adding the 1 which was carried we have 1,10. We write 1 and "carry" 1.

The product $2 \cdot 2 = 4$. Adding 1 we have 10. The product of 2,14 and 2 is 10,13.

Remembering that the actual value of the 1 in the number 12 is 5, we perform the multiplication $2,14 \cdot 10$, where the 1 in 10 has the value 5. The detailed multiplication is then:

$$10 \cdot 4 = 2,00 \qquad (5 \cdot 4 = 20)$$
$$10 \cdot 10 = 2,10 \qquad (5 \cdot 5 = 25)$$
$$10 \cdot 2,00 = 1,00,00 \qquad (5 \cdot 20 = 100)$$

The product of 10 and 2,14 is 1,04,10.

The product of 12 and 2,14 is, then, 2,00,03.

PROBLEMS

1. Add 1,12,04,13 and 10,13,14,03.
2. Add 10,01,13,14; 1,14,12,03; and 11,12,14,10.
3. Subtract 11,13,04 from 13,14,03,04.
4. Multiply 1,13 by 13.

The Chinese, Japanese, and Romans Are Arithmetic Brothers

Strange as it may seem, the arithmetic of the Romans and the arithmetic of the Chinese and Japanese have so much in common that one might suspect that these peoples had common roots. Although such common roots probably never existed, the arithmetic of the Romans and the arithmetic of the Chinese and the Japanese are as identical as Siamese twins. This similarity is a mystery which defies explanation.

The computing devices of the Chinese and of the Japanese are known as the Suan-pan and the Soroban respectively. The construction of these devices is simple. Several wires are strung on a rectangular frame. About two-thirds of the way from the lower edge of the frame a bar is placed across the wires. This bar divides the entire frame into two compartments. On each wire in the lower compartments five beads are strung. Only two beads are strung on the wires in the upper compartment. See Figure 24.

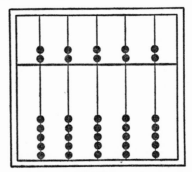

Fig. 24

The five beads in the lower compartment are equal in value to one bead on the same wire in the upper compartment. Thus, when five beads on the same wire are slid down, they must be moved back, and one bead in the upper portion of the same wire must be slid down. This indicates that the number 5 was reached. Note, however, that this operation actually represents the writing of the number 5 in the bi-quinary system of numeration as 10. In other words, for every place value, the sub-place on the left side corresponds to the upper portion of a wire, while the sub-place on the right side corresponds to the lower portion of a wire.

The Chinese and the Japanese counted and computed in a manner very similar to the Roman System. The Chinese, up to the thirteenth century of our era, employed bamboo or ivory sticks for numeration and counting, as well as for calculations. The first nine digits were represented by sticks in a manner suggestive of the bi-quinary system of numeration, as is shown below:

/   //   ///   ////   /////   T   TT   TTT   TTTT
1   2   3   4   5   6   7   8   9

Thus the number 56,893 is represented on the Suan-pan or the Soroban as shown in Figure 25.

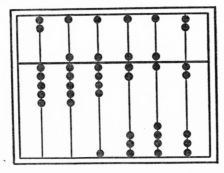

Fig. 25

The number 56,893 is written in the bi-quinary system of numeration as 10,11,13,14,03.

The Chinese and Japanese are very adept in the use of their respective computing devices. A visit to any Chinese laundry (with or without the laundry ticket) would prove to be very instructive.

Some are awed by the complexity of modern electronic computing devices. To the uninitiated these devices seem so uncanny that one is left with the feeling of having seen something which borders on magic. There is, however, nothing magical about these computing devices. The electronic tubes of a digital computer are so constructed that they resemble the Suan-pan or the Soroban in their operation. One tube (or a portion of it) will accept four impulses. The fifth impulse *fills* the tube to more than its capacity and an impulse is sent on to another tube (or a portion of the same tube). The new tube (or the portion of the same tube) can accept only one impulse. The second impulse *fills* the tube to capacity and an impulse is sent to another tube. These operations correspond to the sliding of the beads on the wires.

Columbus Missed This

The Mayans of South America have developed a numeration system which resembles, but is broader in scope than, the Roman system. The origins of the decimal system of numeration is ascribed by many to the fact that man began to count on the fingers of the two hands and, thus, was limited to ten. The Mayans, probably influenced by practical considerations, must have hit on the idea that the use of the toes would extend the first steps in counting. This led to counting to twenty, which in turn led to the development of the *vigesimal* system of numeration, a system based on 20.

One form of the Mayan system, though still related to the base 20, resembles the methods of the Roman, Chinese, and Japanese. The explanation of the similarity may be that counting started with the fingers of one hand, then, as "five" was reached, the fingers of the second hand were used. After the fingers were "used up," the toes also came to be used. Thus, the Mayan system represents an extension of the bi-quinary system of numeration. While the primary counting is limited to "five," that is, as soon as "five" is reached this fact is recorded, the secondary steps are limited to "four." In the bi-quinary system the secondary steps are limited to "two." One form of the Mayan system of numeration is a blend of the four-system and the five-system.

The first twenty numbers, as written by the Mayans and their corresponding numbers in the decimal system and the four-five or *tetra-quinary system* are:

Mayan Numbers	Four-Five Numbers	Decimal Numbers
	0	0
	1	1
	2	2
	3	3
	4	4
	10	5
	11	6
	12	7
	13	8
	14	9
	20	10
	21	11
	22	12
	23	13
	24	14

Mayan Numbers	Four-Five Numbers	Decimal Numbers
☰	30	15
☰ (•)	31	16
☰ (• •)	32	17
☰ (• • •)	33	18
☰ (• • • •)	34	19

The number 20, when written in the four-five system of numeration, is 1,00; the number 100, is 10,00, and 1,00,00 corresponds to the number 400 in the decimal system.

A New Form for the Dozen System*

The dozen, twelve, or duo-decimal system is based on twelve digits, 0, 1, 2, 3, 4, 5, 6, 7, 8, 9, *t* (for *ten*) and *e* (for *eleven*). It is advocated by many because it permits even division by 2, 3, 4, and 6, while the decimal system permits even division by 2 and 5 only.

Counting by *twelves* may be performed in a manner which is similar to the bi-quinary method. We may count by *sixes* and then switch to counting by *twos*. Or, we may count by *fours* and then switch over to counting by *threes*. Thus, we may have either a two-six or a three-four system of numeration.

If we employ the two-six method, we obtain the following:

Two-six Numbers	Decimal Numbers	Duo-decimal Numbers
0	0	0
1	1	1
2	2	2
3	3	3

---

* For a complete description of the "dozen system of numeration" consult A. Bakst, *Mathematics, Its Magic and Mastery*, D. Van Nostrand Co., Inc., New York, 1952, pp. 20-33.

Two-six Numbers	Decimal Numbers	Duo-decimal Numbers
4	4	4
5	5	5
10	6	6
11	7	7
12	8	8
13	9	9
14	10	t
15	11	e

Counting by *twelves* in the three-four system of numera-tion leads to the following:

Three-four Numbers	Decimal Numbers	Duo-decimal Numbers
0	0	0
1	1	1
2	2	2
3	3	3
10	4	4
11	5	5
12	6	6
13	7	7
20	8	8
21	9	9
22	10	t
23	11	e

Twelve, when written in either the two-six or the three-four system of numeration, is 1,00; 1,00,00 corresponds to the decimal number 144 and is written as 100.

PROBLEMS

5. Write in the four-five system of numeration the number which corresponds to 673.
6. Write in the two-six system of numeration the number which corresponds to 589.

7. Write in the three-four system of numeration the number which corresponds to 846.
8. Add 23,31,30,12 and 1,02,32,04 in the four-five system of numeration.
9. Add 1,05,12,11,05 and 12,11,15,01,14 in the two-six system of numeration.
10. Add 2,01,23,02, 10,20,12,13, and 11,12,23,03 in the three-four system of numeration.

Arithmetic for Snow White

History does not record whether Snow White, when she lived with the seven dwarfs, attended school. It is safe to assume that the good elves did not neglect her education, but because the dwarfs had only four fingers on each hand (and presumably four toes on each foot) their counting system must have employed the octal system described in Chapter 5.

If, however, Snow White and the Seven Dwarfs had lived among the Mayans, the method of numeration would have undergone certain modifications. The dwarfs could, then, have counted according to the two-four system of numeration. They also could have counted according to the four, four-four, two-eight, bi-octal system, or the sixteen system.

Below are examples of the numbers which might have occurred in the course of the education of Snow White:

Two-four Numbers	Decimal Numbers	Octal Numbers
0	0	0
1	1	1
2	2	2
3	3	3
10	4	4
11	5	5
12	6	6
13	7	7
1,00	8	10

Bi-octal Numbers	Decimal Numbers	Octal Numbers
0	0	0
1	1	1
2	2	2
3	3	3
4	4	4
5	5	5
6	6	6
7	7	7
10	8	10
11	9	11
12	10	12
13	11	13
14	12	14
15	13	15
16	14	16
17	15	17
1,00	16	20

PROBLEMS

11. Add 1,05,16,07 and 13,12,05,14 in the bi-octal system of numeration.
12. Add 13,03,12,11,01 and 1,12,12,13,10,11 in the two-four system of numeration.
13. Design the computing abacus for the four-five system of numeration.
14. Design the computing abacus for the three-four system of numeration.
15. Design the computing abacus for the bi-octal system of numeration.

Chapter 7

SOMETHING NEW
ABOUT GOESINTOS

Two Ways of Doing the Same Thing

There is an old saw about the right way, the wrong way, and the army way of doing things. Mathematics recognizes only the easy and the hard way. If we are faced with a problem, we may attack it and solve it and forget about it. When a similar problem arises, we may start all over again and labor on it until we solve it. This is the hard way. If, however, we note the characteristic properties of a problem and if we also note the methods which were employed in its solution, new but similar problems offer no special difficulties. This is the easy, or the mathematical, way. Generally, mathematics is not concerned with the solutions of specific problems; it is the method that counts. The specific solutions then become routine matters.

If we wish to learn whether a particular number is evenly divisible by some other number, we may obtain the answer by performing the actual division. If, after the division is performed, there is no remainder, we conclude that the given number is evenly divisible by the other number. We usually say that the number by which we divided "goes into the given number a certain number of times." If we must ascertain whether a different number is divisible by the same divisor, we can perform the actual division again. This, however, is the hard way. Since mathematicians are, by and large, very lazy, they always try to devise gadgets to perform operations which are repeated many times.

In this chapter we shall devise means or gadgets for determining whether a given number is evenly divisible by some other number.

Odd or Even?

An even number is one which is evenly divisible by 2, while an odd number is not divisible by 2. This definition is, however, not complete, for it does not take into account the translation of a number into some other system of numeration. A simple test determines whether a number in the decimal system is even. Any decimal-system number consists of a collection of digits which occupy places assigned definite values. Starting from the right, these places have the values of units, tens, hundreds, thousands, and so on. The divisibility by 2 without a remainder of a number written in this system of numeration depends on one criterion.

If the digit in the units' place is divisible by 2, the entire number is even. Otherwise, the entire number is odd.

For example, the number 217 is odd; 7 is not divisible by 2. Since 6 is divisible by 2, 186 is also divisible by 2.

The test for divisibility without a remainder by 2 for numbers written in the decimal system does not possess the generality which is the usual goal in mathematics. Suppose that a number is written in a system of numeration other than the decimal, will the criterion stated above hold?

Let us consider any system of numeration and call its base a. Any number written in that system may be represented as

$$Aa^n + Ba^{n-1} + Ca^{n-2} + \cdots + Ma + N$$

where $A, B, C, \ldots, M, N$ are the digits, and n represents a number which is associated with the number of value places. Actually this number will have $(n + 1)$ places. If the base a is even, then the even divisibility of the number by 2 depends on the divisibility by 2 of the number N. That this is so may be noted from the fact that the

$$Aa^n + Ba^{n-1} + Ca^{n-2} + \cdots + Ma$$

portion of the number is evenly divisible by 2 because every member of this portion contains a factor a which is evenly divisible by 2. Thus, for example, the number 342,153,442 which is written in the six-system of numeration is even because the base, 6, and the number on the extreme right of the number are both even.

If, however, the base of the system is odd, the evenness of the number cannot be determined by the digit on the extreme right. Since a is odd, each power of a is also odd; although some of the digits may be even and some odd. The odd digits will not affect the powers of a. On the other hand, the even digits, when multiplied by their associated powers of a, make the products even. It follows that a number will be even if it contains an even number of odd digits, and it will be odd if it does contain an odd number of odd digits. For example, 1,425,783,813 which is written in the nine-system of numeration is even, that is, it is evenly divisible by 2. The odd digits are 1, 5, 7, 3, 1, 3, and there are six of them, and six is an even number.

To simplify the statements concerning the systems of numeration and to conserve space, we shall write the base of the system of numeration at the right of the number. The symbol $524_{(7)}$ will signify that the number 524 is written in the seven-system of numeration. The number $105,672_{(8)}$ is written in the eight-system.

One Less Than the Base

When a number is written in the decimal system of numeration the question of its divisibility by 9 without a remainder is usually resolved according to the following scheme. This number is so written that it can be represented as

$$A10^n + B10^{n-1} + C10^{n-2} + \cdots M10 + N$$

where $A, B, C, \ldots , M, N$ are the digits.

The base 10 may be represented as $10 = 9 + 1$. Then the representation of the number may be rewritten as follows:

$$A(9 + 1)^n + B(9 + 1)^{n-1} + C(9 + 1)^{n-2}$$
$$+ \cdots + M(9 + 1) + N$$

If the expressions in the parentheses were raised to their respective powers, there will be collections containing 9 as factors with the exception of one term for each expression; this term will be 1. When multiplied by their respective digits, these terms will be represented by the sum $A + B + C + \cdots + M + N$. If this sum is evenly divisible by 9, the number is divisible by 9 without a remainder. Thus, the criterion for the divisibility by 9 may be stated as follows:

If the sum of the digits of the number (which is written in the decimal system of numeration) is evenly divisible by 9, then the number is also divisible by 9 without a remainder.

For example, $2,167,892,352_{(10)}$ is evenly divisible by 9 because

$$2 + 1 + 6 + 7 + 8 + 9 + 2 + 3 + 5 + 2 = 45$$

and 45 is divisible by 9 without a remainder.

In the case of the base 10, the number 9 is "one less than the base." The examination of the even divisibility by 9 of a number, which is written in the decimal system of numeration, performed above suggests the possibility of generalization of the same procedure to include *any* base. For this purpose we shall replace the base 10 with the symbol a which will denote any base. The expression for a number which is written in the a system of numeration is

$$Aa^n + Ba^{n-1} + Ca^{n-2} + \cdots Ma + N$$

The number a, which represents the base of the system of numeration, may be represented as $a = (a - 1) + 1$. Then the expression for the number may be represented as

$$A[(a - 1) + 1]^n + B[(a - 1) + 1]^{n-1}$$
$$+ C[(a - 1) + 1]^{n-2} + \cdots + M[(a - 1) + 1] + N$$

If the expressions in the brackets are raised to their respective powers, there will be collections containing $(a-1)$ as factors with the exception of one term for each expression; this term will be 1. When multiplied by their respective digits, these terms may be represented by the sum $A + B + C + \cdots + M + N$. If this sum is evenly divisible by $(a-1)$, then the given number is divisible by $(a-1)$ without a remainder. Thus, the criterion for the even divisibility by $(a-1)$, where the number a represents the base of the system of numeration, may be stated as follows:

If the sum of the digits of a number written in a system of numeration whose base is a is evenly divisible by (a — 1), the number is also evenly divisible by (a — 1).

For example, $2,535,253_{(6)}$ is evenly divisible by 5 because

$$2 + 5 + 3 + 5 + 2 + 5 + 3 = 25$$

the number is written in the six-system of numeration, and 25 is divisible by 5 $(6 - 1 = 5)$ without a remainder.

Also, $43,516,401_{(7)}$ is evenly divisible by 6 because

$$4 + 3 + 5 + 1 + 6 + 4 + 0 + 1 = 24$$

the number is written in the seven-system of numeration, and 24 is divisible by 6 $(7 - 1 = 6)$ without a remainder.

It should be also noted that when a number is evenly divisible by another number it is also evenly divisible by the factors of that other number. Thus, when a number is divisible by 9 without a remainder it is also evenly divisible by 3. When a number is evenly divisible by 6, it is also evenly divisible by 2 and by 3.

We may then formulate another criterion for even divisibility. It is concerned with the divisibility by 3.

If the sum of the digits of a number and the base of that number diminished by 1 (a — 1) are both evenly divisible by 3, the number is also evenly divisible by 3.

One More Than the Base

When a number is written in the decimal system of numeration it is possible to determine whether this number is evenly divisible by 11 without performing the long division. This number can be represented as

$$A10^n + B10^{n-1} + C10^{n-2} + \cdots + M10 + N$$

where $A, B, C, \ldots, M, N$ are the digits.

The base 10 may be represented as $10 = 11 - 1$. Then the representation of the number may be rewritten as follows:

$$A(11 - 1)^n + B(11 - 1)^{n-1} + C(11 - 1)^{n-2}$$
$$+ \cdots + M(11 - 1) + N$$

If the expressions in the parentheses are raised to their respective powers, there will be collections containing 11 as factors with the exception of one term for each expression; this term will be 1. But in each case it will be a negative 1, (-1), raised to its respective power. If the power to which (-1) is raised is even, as for example 2, 4, 6, $\ldots$, the result is a positive 1, that is, $(+1)$. If the power to which (-1) is raised is odd, the result is a negative 1, that is, (-1). Since the powers of $(11 - 1)$ are represented by consecutive integers, the positive 1's and the negative 1's will alternate. Thus in the sum of $A, B, C, \ldots, M$, and N the positive and negative terms will alternate. The positive terms may be in the even positions and the negative terms may be in the odd positions, or vice versa.

The sum of the terms $A, B, C, \ldots, M, N$ with their respective signs will form the criterion for the even divisibility by 11. If this sum is evenly divisible by 11, the number will be evenly divisible by 11. Furthermore, it is immaterial whether a number is positive or negative when its divisibility without a remainder by some other number is considered. The criterion for the even divisibility by 11 of a number which is written in the decimal system of numeration may be stated as follows:

If the difference between the sum of the digits in the even positions and the sum of the digits in the odd positions is evenly divisible by 11, the whole number is evenly divisible by 11.

For example, to see whether $327{,}819{,}704{,}563_{(10)}$ is evenly divisible by 11, we add $3 + 7 + 1 + 7 + 4 + 6 = 28$ and $2 + 8 + 9 + 0 + 5 + 3 = 27$. Since $26 - 27 = -1$, and -1 is not divisible by 11, $327{,}819{,}704{,}563_{(10)}$ is not evenly divisible by 11.

To test $2{,}530{,}968{,}154{,}209_{(10)}$ for its even divisibility by 11, we add $2 + 3 + 9 + 8 + 5 + 2 + 9 = 38$ and $5 + 0 + 6 + 1 + 4 + 0 = 16$. Since $38 - 16 = 22$, and 22 is evenly divisible by 11, $2{,}530{,}968{,}154{,}209_{(10)}$ is divisible by 11 without a remainder.

The number 11 is one more than the base 10. The examination of the even divisibility by 11 of a number, which is written in the decimal system of numeration, performed above suggests the possibility of generalization of the same procedure to include *any* base. For this purpose we shall replace the base 10 with a symbol a which will denote any base. The expression for a number which is written in a system of numeration whose base is a is

$$Aa^n + Ba^{n-1} + Ca^{n-2} + \cdots + Ma + N$$

The number a which represents the base of the system of numeration may be represented as $a = (a + 1) - 1$. Then the expression for the number in the system of numeration whose base is a may be represented as

$$A[(a + 1) - 1]^n + B[(a + 1) - 1]^{n-1}$$
$$+ C[(a + 1) - 1]^{n-2} + \cdots + M[(a + 1) - 1] + N$$

If the expressions in the brackets are raised to their respective powers, there will be collections containing $a + 1$ as factors with the exception of one term for each expression; this term will be 1. But in each case it will be a negative 1, or -1, raised to its respective power. If the power of -1 is even, the result is a positive 1, or $+1$. If the power of -1 is odd, the result is a negative 1, or -1. Since the powers of $[(a+1)-1]$ are represented by consecutive integers, the positive 1's and the negative 1's will alternate. Thus in the sum of $A, B, C, \ldots, M$, and N the positive and negative terms will alternate. The positive terms may be in either the even or the odd positions.

The sum of the terms $A, B, C, \ldots, M, N$ with their respective signs will be the criterion for testing the even divisibility by $a+1$. If this sum is evenly divisible by $a+1$, the given number will be divisible by $a+1$ without a remainder. Whether a number is positive or negative makes no difference when the question concerning its even divisibility by some other number is considered. The criterion for the even divisibility by $a+1$ of a number which is written in a system of numeration whose base is a may be stated as follows: If the difference between the sum of the digits in the even positions and the sum of the digits in the odd positions is evenly divisible by the base plus 1 $(a+1)$, the whole number is also evenly divisible by that number.

For example, we know that $503{,}655{,}215{,}462_{(7)}$ is divisible by 8 because

$$5 + 3 + 5 + 2 + 5 + 6 = 26$$
$$0 + 6 + 5 + 1 + 4 + 2 = 18$$

and $$26 - 18 = 8$$

The difference between the two sums is evenly divisible by the base plus 1, that is, by 8.

We can see that the number $5{,}189{,}238{,}742{,}566_{(9)}$ is evenly divisible by 10; since

$$5 + 8 + 2 + 8 + 4 + 5 + 6 = 38$$
and $$1 + 9 + 3 + 7 + 2 + 6 = 28$$

and $39 - 29 = 10$. The difference is evenly divisible by 10, which is the base of the number plus 1 $(9 + 1 = 10)$. We know the number $5{,}189{,}238{,}742{,}566_{(9)}$ is also evenly divisible by 2 and by 5, because 2 and 5 are factors of 10.

The reader should note, however, that the even division by $a + 1$ of a number which is written in a system of numeration whose base is a implies that the number $a + 1$, when represented in its own system of numeration, is written as 11. A number a, when it is written in the system of numeration whose base is a, is always represented as 10. For example, if the system of numeration has the base 7, then 7 is represented by 10, and $7 + 1$ is represented by 11. Thus, when the system of numeration has the base 9 and the even divisibility by 10 is investigated, the number 10 is represented by 11.

On Either Side of the Base

If a number is evenly divisible by some divisor, this same number is evenly divisible by the factors of that divisor. For example, if a number is evenly divisible by 12, it is also evenly divisible by 2, 3, 4, and 6. For example:

$$204 \div 12 = 17, \quad 204 \div 2 = 102, \quad 204 \div 3 = 68,$$
$$204 \div 4 = 51, \quad 204 \div 6 = 34.$$

If a number is written in the decimal system of numeration, its even divisibility by 33 or by 99 is determined in terms of the divisibility without a remainder of this number by 3 and 11 or by 9 and 11 respectively. We know the number $1,729,572,471_{(10)}$ is evenly divisible by 9, because

$$1 + 7 + 2 + 9 + 5 + 7 + 2 + 4 + 7 + 1 = 45$$

and 45 is evenly divisible by 9. This same number is also evenly divisible by 11. Note that

$$1 + 2 + 5 + 2 + 7 = 17 \quad \text{and} \quad 7 + 9 + 7 + 4 + 1 = 28$$

and $28 - 17 = 11$. Thus the number $1,729,572,471_{(10)}$ is evenly divisible by the product of 9 and 11, that is, by 99. Furthermore, it is evenly divisible by 3 and by 33.

No matter what system of numeration is involved, the even divisibility of a number by a divisor whose factors are "one more than the base" and "one less than the base" is determined by the procedure described in the case of the divisor 99 in the decimal system. It should, however, be noted that the number which is equal to "one less than the base" possesses the same properties as the number 9 in the decimal system of numeration, while the number which is "one more than the base is always represented by 11. Thus, if the base of the system of numeration is 8 then the divisor which corresponds to $99_{(10)}$ is $77_{(8)}$.

For example, we know the number $156{,}312{,}541{,}305_{(7)}$ is evenly divisible by 6 because

$$1 + 5 + 6 + 3 + 1 + 2 + 5 + 4 + 1 + 3 + 0 + 5 = 36$$

and 36 is evenly divisible by 6. Furthermore,

$$1 + 6 + 1 + 5 + 1 + 0 = 14$$
and $$5 + 3 + 2 + 4 + 3 + 5 = 22$$

and $22 - 14 = 8$. When written in the seven-system of numeration, the number 8 is represented by $11_{(7)}$. Thus, the number $156{,}312{,}541{,}305_{(7)}$ is evenly divisible by $66_{(7)}$. When translated into the decimal system of numeration, the number $156{,}312{,}541{,}305_{(7)}$ is evenly divisible by 48, because $6 \times 8 = 48$.

Any Divisor, Please

The determination of the even divisibility of a number written in any system of numeration by any divisor (written in the same system of numeration) may be generalized so that one rule may be applied to all cases. Such a generalization will eliminate the specific rules for specific situations and specific numbers.

To develop the generalized rule, we will examine the properties of numbers when they are written in the most generalized form, in symbolic representation. If the base of a system of numeration is denoted by the symbol k, and the number contains $n + 1$ digits, the number can be written

$$Ak^n + Bk^{n-1} + Ck^{n-2} + Dk^{n-3} + \cdots + Mk^2 + Nk + R$$

where the symbols $A, B, C, D, \ldots, M, N, R$ denote the digits. These digits may all be distinct and different, although the equality of some or of all of the numbers represented by these digits is not excluded. For example, the number $23{,}567{,}189_{(10)}$ may be written

$$(2 \cdot 10^7) + (3 \cdot 10^6) + (5 \cdot 10^5) + (6 \cdot 10^4)$$
$$+ (7 \cdot 10^3) + (1 \cdot 10^2) + (8 \cdot 10) + 9$$

When two numbers a and b are raised to the same power, which is represented by a positive whole number n, the difference of these two powers, that is, $a^n - b^n$ is evenly divisible by the difference of the two numbers, that is, by $a - b$. For example, if $a = 6$ and $b = 2$, while $n = 3$, or 4, or 5, or any other number,

$6^3 - 2^3 = 216 - 8 = 208$, and $6 - 2 = 4$, and $208 \div 4 = 52$
$6^4 - 2^4 = 1{,}296 - 32 = 1{,}264$, and $1{,}264 \div 4 = 316$
$6^5 - 2^5 = 7{,}776 - 64 = 7{,}712$, and $7{,}712 \div 4 = 1{,}928$

If the symbols a and b represent two different bases, the numbers which are written in these two systems may be represented symbolically as

$$A_1a^n + B_1a^{n-1} + C_1a^{n-2} + D_1a^{n-3} + \cdots + M_1a^2 + N_1a + R_1$$

and

$$A_2b^n + B_2b^{n-1} + C_2b^{n-2} + D_2b^{n-3} + \cdots + M_2b^2 + N_2b + R_2$$

The subscripts of the symbols $A, B, C, D, \ldots, M, N, R$ indicate that these symbols represent different digits. The symbol n indicates that both numbers consist of the same number of digits. This latter fact is very important.

Let us assume that we have two numbers which are written in two different systems of numeration. These numbers have the same number of digits, and the digits are not only the same, but they appear in the same sequence. For example, we may have $13{,}432_{(5)}$ and $13{,}432_{(7)}$. The first is written in the five-system of numeration, while the second is written in the seven-system. The general expressions for two such numbers are written as follows:

$$Aa^n + Ba^{n-1} + Ca^{n-2} + Da^{n-3} + \cdots + Ma^2 + Na + R$$

and

$$Ab^n + Bb^{n-1} + Cb^{n-2} + Db^{n-3} + \cdots + Mb^2 + Nb + R$$

The difference of these two symbolic expressions is

$$A(a^n - b^n) + B(a^{n-1} - b^{n-1}) + C(a^{n-2} - b^{n-2})$$
$$+ D(a^{n-3} - b^{n-3}) + \cdots + M(a^2 - b^2) + N(a - b)$$

This difference is evenly divisible by $(a - b)$ because each term in this difference contains $(a - b)$ as a factor. If the number

$$Aa^n + Ba^{n-1} + Ca^{n-2} + Da^{n-3} + \cdots + Ma^2 + Na + R$$

is to be evenly divisible by $(a - b)$, the number

$$Ab^n + Bb^{n-1} + Cb^{n-2} + Db^{n-3} + \cdots + Mb^2 + Nb + R$$

must also be evenly divisible by $(a - b)$.

Suppose that we wish to ascertain whether the number $162_{(10)}$ is evenly divisible by 7. Since $162_{(10)}$ is written in the decimal system of numeration, $a = 10$, and since $a - b = 7$, that is, $(10 - b = 7)$, we get $b = 3$. Thus, we must compute the value of $162_{(3)}$. Since $(1 \cdot 3^2) + (6 \cdot 3) + 2 = 9 + 18 + 2 = 29$, and 29 is not evenly divisible by 7, $162_{(10)}$ is not divisible by 7 without a remainder.

The writing $162_{(3)}$ may seem to be a violation of the principle of writing numbers in different systems of numeration. In the three-system there are only three digits, namely, 0, 1, and 2. The digit "6" does not belong to the three-system of numeration. However, such a violation should not be considered serious. It is employed for the purposes of computations only.

To see whether the number $224_{(10)}$ is evenly divisible by 7, we compute the value of $224_{(3)}$. Since

$$(2 \cdot 3^2) + (2 \cdot 3) + 4 = 18 + 6 + 4 = 28$$

and 28 is evenly divisible by 7, then $224_{(10)}$ is divisible by 7 without a remainder.

The test for even divisibility developed above holds for numbers with any number of digits. For example, to test for the even divisibility by 7 of the number $34,562_{(10)}$ we compute the value of $34,562_{(3)}$ and get

$$(3 \cdot 3^4) + (4 \cdot 3^3) + (5 \cdot 3^2) + (6 \cdot 3) + 2$$

or $\qquad 243 + 108 + 45 + 18 + 2 = 416$

Computing the value of $416_{(3)}$ we obtain

$$(4 \cdot 3^2) + (1 \cdot 3) + 6 = 36 + 3 + 6 = 45$$

Because 45 is not evenly divisible by 7, we know $34,562_{(10)}$ is not evenly divisible by 7. As a matter of fact, $34,562 \div 7 = 4,937 +$ remainder 3. Also, $416 \div 7 = 59 +$ remainder 3. Note that the remainders after the divisions by 7 are all equal to 3. This remainder corresponds to the symbol R in the algebraic expressions given above.

The reader will note that the tests for even divisibility may be carried out consecutively until a small number is obtained. As a matter of fact, we could have carried out the test for the even divisibility by 7 of the number $45_{(10)}$. Computing the value of $45_{(3)}$ we have

$$(4 \cdot 3) + 5 = 12 + 5 = 17$$

We could then have tested the even divisibility by 7 of the number $17_{(10)}$ by computing the value of $17_{(3)}$ and would have obtained $(1 \cdot 3) + 7 = 10$. At every instance the result indicates that the even divisibility by 7 is impossible.

The method for testing of even divisibility which has been described here is applicable to any divisor. The test for the even divisibility by 9 follows this same scheme. In this case $a = 10$, and $b = 1$, while $a - b = 9$. Note that, since $b = 1$, the test for the even divisibility by 9 of a number written in the decimal system of numeration resolves to the obtaining of the sum of the digits of the number. The test for the even divisibility by 11 of a number written in the decimal system of numeration considers $a = 10$ and $b = -1$, while $a - b = 10 - (-1) = 10 + 1 = 11$. In this case the base of the system of numeration is a negative number, namely, (-1).

In a similar manner we can test for even divisibility by 13 of a number written in the decimal system of numeration. For example, to see whether $379_{(10)}$ is evenly divisible by 13 we compute the value of $379_{(-3)}$ (remembering that $a = 10$ and $b = -3$) and we obtain

$$3 \cdot (-3)^2 + 7 \cdot (-3) + 9 = 3 \cdot 9 - 7 \cdot 3 + 9$$

or $$27 - 21 + 9 = 15$$

Since 15 is not evenly divisible by 13 ($15 \div 13 = 1 +$ remainder 2), $379_{(10)}$ is not evenly divisible by 13 ($379 \div 13 = 27 +$ remainder 2). The remainders after both divisions are performed are 2.

When the method for the testing of even divisibility by any number was developed, a new fact was introduced, namely, that bases for systems of numeration need not be confined to positive numbers. A negative base is just as legitimate as a positive base. Because negative bases have not been used does not mean that they are taboo in mathematics.

PROBLEMS

1. Test to see whether following numbers are odd or even.
   (a) $12,303_{(4)}$; (b) $13,202_{(4)}$; (c) $24,301_{(5)}$; (d) $57,-623_{(8)}$; (e) $425,618_{(9)}$; (f) $ee,tte_{(12)}$.
2. Test the following numbers to see whether they can be evenly divided by their divisors.
   (a) $22,312_{(4)}$ by 3; (b) $423,112_{(5)}$ by 4; (c) $56,064_{(8)}$ by 7; (d) $877,503_{(9)}$ by 8; (e) $31,404_{(5)}$ by 6; (f) $55,-634_{(7)}$ by 8; (g) $823,114_{(9)}$ by 10; (h) $23,145_{(10)}$ by 7; (i) $55,342_{(10)}$ by 8; (j) $427,126_{(10)}$ by 13.

Chapter 8

HARNESSING
FATHER TIME

Is It the Same Time as Yesterday?

We shall not concern ourselves with the definition of *time*. Since man began to philosophize, no two men have ever agreed as to what *time* is. So, we will leave the problem of time (or what it is) to the philosophers. Philosophers notwithstanding, time can cause loads of grief to unsuspecting mortals.

You look at a watch (or clock) and tell your friend: "I will meet you (and you name the place) tomorrow at the same time as today." Your friend takes your word for it. But, try as you may, time works havoc with your promise. "The same time as today" just does not happen tomorrow. But, you will say, the day is still 24 hours long. How can it then happen that "the same time as today" is really *not the same?*

The length of the day (which we accept as being 24 hours) is measured in terms of the earth's revolution on its axis. It is generally accepted that this revolution is uniform and that its rate is unchangeable (at least within the scope of a single human life). The length of the day is, however, marked in terms of two distinct criteria. An astronomer observes a star and notes its position in relation to the surface of the earth. The star is usually observed as it reaches the highest point in the sky during one revolution of the earth. Then, a day later, the passage of the star through the same

point is observed. In a similar manner the passage of the
sun is observed. Unfortunately, the intervals between the
passages of these two celestial bodies, as expressed in time
measure, are not the same. If the interval between the two
passages of the sun is taken as 24 hours, the interval between
the two passages of the star is equal to 23 hours, 56 minutes,
and 4 seconds. In other words, the "star time" or the "star
day" is approximately 3 minutes and 56 seconds shorter
than the solar time or the "solar day." The discrepancy, and
it is observable, is due to the fact that the earth moves
around the sun. The forward motion of the earth accounts
for the delay of about 3 minutes and 56 seconds in the sun's
passage through the highest point. Thus, if your friend is
an astronomer, he will point out to you, as you meet him,
that you are about 3 minutes and 56 seconds early. Our
watches and clocks are attuned to the solar time.

The relations between the "star day" and the "solar day"
are expressed numerically as follows:

1 solar day = 1 star day + 3 minutes 56.56 seconds
of star time.
1 star day = 1 solar day − 3 minutes 55.91 seconds
of solar time.

To attain some uniformity in measurement of time, astron-
omers introduce other artificial criteria which *equate* (or
smooth out) the intervals between the completed rotations
of the earth on its axis. Thus, time measurements are not
as simple as they may seem, and exactness is never attained.
But the determination of the length of the day is only the
first woe of the measures of time.

How Long Is the Year?

We assume that most years are 365 days long, and that
every fourth year has 366 days. This may be simple from
the point of view of the average citizen. But a year is not
either 365 or 366 days long. A year is defined as the interval

of time between two passages of the earth through the same point on its orbit in relation to the sun. This is, however, the definition of one kind of a year. This is known as the solar year. It is 365 days, 6 hours, 9 minutes, and 9.6 seconds of mean (equated) solar time. Thus, the calendar year, which is 365 days long, is shorter than the solar year, and the calendar leap year is longer than the solar year. There is another year, known as the tropical year. The tropical year is 365 days, 5 hours, 48 minutes, and 46 seconds long. The tropical year is associated with the return of the seasons. It is agreed, however, that the length of the solar year (in terms of mean solar days) is approximately 365.2422 mean solar days. If we consider star days, the length of the year is approximately 366.2422 star days.

If the length of a year were 365.25 days, the introduction of an additional day once every four years, making the fourth year a leap year, would completely compensate for the discrepancy. But 0.25 is not equal to 0.2422. In other words, the discrepancy is approximately 0.0078 day. It may seem to be an insignificant quantity. Nevertheless, this small quantity was (and still is) sufficient to cause much trouble in calendar making. In a thousand years, this discrepancy is equal to 7.8 days.

When Does New Year's Day Occur?

A calendar year (except for leap year) is 52 weeks and one day long. If New Year's day in some year following a leap year occurs on a Sunday, then the next New Year's day will occur on a Monday. The next following New Year's day will occur on a Tuesday. The New Year's day of the leap year will occur on a Wednesday. Since there are 366 days in a leap year, the next New Year's day will occur on a Friday, and not on a Thursday as one would expect. Thus, as far as New Year's days are concerned, their regular sequence is interrupted every four years (except during the years whose numbers are not evenly divisible by 400). If

January 1, 1953, was on Thursday, then January 1, 1955, will be on Saturday, and January 1, 1956, will be on Sunday. However, January 1, 1957, will be on Tuesday.

What Day of the Week Is It?

Suppose that February 5 falls on Monday. On what day of the week will September 15 fall? In order to determine on which day September 15 will fall (we shall assume that this is not a leap year), we must determine first the number of days between February 4 and September 15. This information may be learned from the tables on pages 88 and 89 by the following procedure:

1. On the line marked February and in the "date column" marked "4" we find that February 4 is the 35th day of the year. On the line for September and in the "date column" marked "15," we find that September 15 is the 258th day of the year.
2. Obtain the difference: 258 − 35 = 223.
3. Since there are seven days in a week, divide 223 by 7. We have then: 223 ÷ 7 = 31 + remainder 6.
4. The remainder 6 indicates that the day on which September 15 falls is the sixth day "after Monday." Thus, September 15 will fall on Sunday. ("After Monday" means that the count begins with Tuesday.)

In the case of leap year, one day must be added after February 28 in order to account for February 29.

PROBLEMS

1. March 15 (in a leap year) falls on Wednesday. On what day of the week will August 21 fall?
2. June 8 (not in a leap year) falls on a Sunday. On what day of the week will December 25 fall?

The rules for obtaining the days of the week may be extended so that the given dates need not be in one year. For

DATE	1	2	3	4	5	6	7	8	9	10	11	12	13	14	15	16
JANUARY	1	2	3	4	5	6	7	8	9	10	11	12	13	14	15	16
FEBRUARY	32	33	34	35	36	37	38	39	40	41	42	43	44	45	46	47
MARCH	60	61	62	63	64	65	66	67	68	69	70	71	72	73	74	75
APRIL	91	92	93	94	95	96	97	98	99	100	101	102	103	104	105	106
MAY	121	122	123	124	125	126	127	128	129	130	131	132	133	134	135	136
JUNE	152	153	154	155	156	157	158	159	160	161	162	163	164	165	166	167
JULY	182	183	184	185	186	187	188	189	190	191	192	193	194	195	196	197
AUGUST	213	214	215	216	217	218	219	220	221	222	223	224	225	226	227	228
SEPTEMBER	244	245	246	247	248	249	250	251	252	253	254	255	256	257	258	259
OCTOBER	274	275	276	277	278	279	280	281	282	283	284	285	286	287	288	289
NOVEMBER	305	306	307	308	309	310	311	312	313	314	315	316	317	318	319	320
DECEMBER	335	336	337	338	339	340	341	342	343	344	345	346	347	348	349	350

DATE	17	18	19	20	21	22	23	24	25	26	27	28	29	30	31
JANUARY	17	18	19	20	21	22	23	24	25	26	27	28	29	30	31
FEBRUARY	48	49	50	51	52	53	54	55	56	57	58	59			
MARCH	76	77	78	79	80	81	82	83	84	85	86	87	88	89	90
APRIL	107	108	109	110	111	112	113	114	115	116	117	118	119	120	
MAY	137	138	139	140	141	142	143	144	145	146	147	148	149	150	151
JUNE	168	169	170	171	172	173	174	175	176	177	178	179	180	181	
JULY	198	199	200	201	202	203	204	205	206	207	208	209	210	211	212
AUGUST	229	230	231	232	233	234	235	236	237	238	239	240	241	242	243
SEPTEMBER	260	261	262	263	264	265	266	267	268	269	270	271	272	273	
OCTOBER	290	291	292	293	294	295	296	297	298	299	300	301	302	303	304
NOVEMBER	321	322	323	324	325	326	327	328	329	330	331	332	333	334	
DECEMBER	351	352	353	354	355	356	357	358	359	360	361	362	363	364	365

example, if February 4 falls on a Monday of one year, and September 15 is in the following year (none of the years are leap years), the calculations are performed as follows:

1. On the line for the month of February and in the "date column" for the 4, we find that February 4 is the 35th day. On the line for September and in the "date column" marked "15," we find that September 15 is the 258th day.
2. Obtain the difference: 258 − 35 = 223.
3. Since the two dates occur in consecutive years we must add 365 to the difference obtained in 2 above. Thus, we have 223 + 365 = 588.
4. Since there are seven days in a week, divide 588 by 7: (588 ÷ 7 = 84).
5. We know that September 15 in the next year will also fall on a Monday since there was no remainder after the division.

A Formula for Finding the Day of the Week from a Given Date

The calendar now in almost universal use is known as the Gregorian Calendar. It was introduced by Pope Gregory XII in 1582 when he decided to rectify the error in the Julian Calendar (introduced by Julius Caesar). Because the Vernal Equinox (the sun is passing through the celestial equator from the southern to the northern hemisphere) occurred on March 11, in 1582, Pope Gregory XII ordered that 10 days be suppressed from the calendar dates in that year so that the Vernal Equinox would fall on March 21, as it should. When he proclaimed the calendar reform, he formulated the rules regarding the leap years.

The Gregorian Calendar is based on the adjusted value of the solar year and also the tropical year because their values do not differ significantly. This value is taken to be approximately 365.2425 days long. For the purposes of calculations of the days of the week we shall have to assume that the Gregorian Calendar could have been effective from year 1, although it was introduced in 1582. Naturally, the first question which is posed concerns the day of the week on which January 1 of year 1 fell. This day may be determined as follows:

We know that January 1, 1952, fell on Wednesday. In terms of the value of the solar (or tropical) year the number of days which have elapsed since January 1 of the year 1 is

$$1951 \cdot 365.2425 = 712588.1275$$

Discarding the decimal portion of the product, we learn that 712,588 days have elapsed since January 1 of the year 1. Dividing this number by 7 we get 101,798 with a remainder of 2. The remainder indicates that two days should be counted from Wednesday. In this case the counting should be done backward because our calculations refer to the past. Thus January 1 of the year 1 in the Gregorian Calendar fell on Monday. It is important that this be kept in mind when the formula for the calculation of the day of the week from a given date is employed.

When using the formula one must also remember that the regular year, which is 365 days long, consists of 52 weeks and 1 day. A leap year consists of 52 weeks and 2 days. Instead of counting the actual number of days which have elapsed since January 1 of the year 1, we will count the number of excess days over weeks which have elapsed and to their number we must add the number of days which have elapsed since January 1 of the given year. This total must be divided by 7, and the remainder will indicate the number of days which must be counted (forward) from Monday. Thus, the formula may be stated as follows (we shall denote Monday by the number 1):

1 + the remainder of the division by 7 of (the number of years which have elapsed thus far + the number of

leap years which have occurred since year 1 + the number of days which have elapsed since January 1 of the given year) = the number of days of the week (the count starts with Monday).

The calculation of the number of leap years must take into account the fact that those years, whose number ends with two zeros, which are not divisible by 400 are not leap years. Thus, 1200, 1600, 2000 are leap years, while 1100, 1300, 1400, 1500, 1700, 1800, 1900 are not leap years. From the total number of leap years a certain number of leap years must be subtracted. The following example will illustrate the application of the foregoing formula.

On what day of the week will Christmas Day 1954 fall?

The additions are performed as follows:

The number for Monday, January 1, 1   1

Number of years which have elapsed   1953

Number of leap years which have elapsed $\dfrac{1953}{4}$ 488

Less the century-leap years . . . . $19 - \dfrac{19}{4} \;\; \dfrac{15}{473}$ 473

Number of days between January 1, 1954 and December 25, 1954   359

                                                   3786

Dividing 3786 by 7 gives us 540 with a remainder of 6.

Thus, Christmas Day in 1954 will fall on Saturday. Counting from Monday, Saturday is the sixth day.

The Perpetual Calendar

The formula for discovering the day of the week from a given date may be called a "perpetual calendar." The problem of the perpetual calendar occupied the attention of many mathematicians, and many of them devoted considerable attention to calculating the date of Easter. All church holidays fall on a definite date. The ecclesiastical rule regarding Easter is, however, rather complicated. Easter must fall on the first Sunday after the first full moon which occurs after the Vernal (the Spring) Equinox.

The Perpetual Calendar given on the following pages is based on the method developed by the German mathematician Gauss. This calendar was further arranged by a German mathematician H. Schubert. He also devised the Easter Date Calendar which is also given on the following pages.

Instructions for the use of the Perpetual Calendar and for the use of the Easter Date Calendar are printed with the calendars. To ascertain the day of the week on which Columbus discovered America, that is, October 12, 1492, we proceed as follows: We note that this was an Old Style date. The century is 14. We locate the year 92. The intersection of the row "14" with the column "92" yields the letter "f." In Table II we locate the position of the letter "f" on the line for "October." The intersection of the column of the letter "f" with the line of the number 12 gives the letter "F." Thus, Columbus discovered America on Friday.

On what day will Christmas of 1954 fall? This is a New Style date. The intersection of the column headed "54" with the row marked "19" yields the letter "c." In Table II we locate the letter "c" in the line for "December." The intersection of the column "c" with the line 25 gives the letters "Sa." Thus, Christmas Day in 1954 will fall on Saturday.

The Perpetual Calendar may be employed in reverse order. For example, we may ascertain the date of Labor Day in 1954. We proceed as follows: In Table I we find that the intersection of the column "54" with the row "19" gives the letter "c." Table II indicates that the column headed "c" in the line for the month of "September" contains the letter "M" in the line of dates 6, 13, 20, and 27. Labor Day is the first Monday in September. Thus, in 1954 Labor Day will fall on September 6.

Using the Easter Date Calendar requires also using the Perpetual Calendar. For example, the Easter Date for the

OLD STYLE CENTURIES — I

0 ..	7 ..	14 ..	c	d	e	f	g	a	b
1 ..	8 ..	15 ..	b	c	d	e	f	g	a
2 ..	9 ..	16 ..	a	b	c	d	e	f	g
3 ..	10 ..	17 ..	g	a	b	c	d	e	f
4 ..	11 ..	18 ..	f	g	a	b	c	d	e
5 ..	12 ..	19 ..	e	f	g	a	b	c	d
6 ..	13 ..	20 ..	d	e	f	g	a	b	c

REMARKS

1. The numbers in bold face italic type [*56*, *64*] indicate leap years in the New Style.

2. Years divisible by 400 are leap years in the New Style.

3. The first day of the New Style accepted by the Catholic Church —October 15, 1582.

4. The First day of the New Style accepted in Protestant Germany, March 1, 1700.

YEARS IN CENTURIES

00	01	02	03		*04*	05
06	07		*08*	09	10	11
	12	13	14	15		*16*
17	18	19		*20*	21	22
23		*24*	25	26	27	
28	29	30	31		*32*	33
34	35		*36*	37	38	39
	40	41	42	43		*44*
45	46	47		*48*	49	50
51		*52*	53	54	55	
56	57	58	59		*60*	61
62	63		*64*	65	66	67
	68	69	70	71		*72*
73	74	75		*76*	77	78
79		*80*	81	82	83	
84	85	86	87		*88*	89
90	91		*92*	93	94	95
	96	97	98	99		

NEW STYLE CENTURIES — I

26 ..	22 ..	18 ..	a	b	c	d	e	f	g
25 ..	21 ..	17 ..	c	d	e	f	g	a	b
24 ..	20 ..	16 ..	e	f	g	a	b	c	d
23 ..	19 ..	15 ..	f	g	a	b	c	d	e

PERPETUAL CALENDAR

II

LEAP YEAR JANUARY	g	a	b	c	d	e	f
LEAP YEAR FEBRUARY	d	e	f	g	a	b	c
January	f	g	a	b	c	d	e
February	c	d	e	f	g	a	b
March	c	d	e	f	g	a	b
April	g	a	b	c	d	e	f
May	e	f	g	a	b	c	d
June	b	c	d	e	f	g	a
July	g	a	b	c	d	e	f
August	d	e	f	g	a	b	c
September	a	b	c	d	e	f	g
October	f	g	a	b	c	d	e
November	c	d	e	f	g	a	b
December	a	b	c	d	e	f	g
1. 8. 15. 22. 29.	M	Tu	W	Th	F	Sa	S
2. 9. 16. 23. 30.	Tu	W	Th	F	Sa	S	M
3. 10. 17. 24. 31.	W	Th	F	Sa	S	M	Tu
4. 11. 18. 25.	Th	F	Sa	S	M	Tu	W
5. 12. 19. 26.	F	Sa	S	M	Tu	W	Th
6. 13. 20. 27.	Sa	S	M	Tu	W	Th	F
7. 14. 21. 28.	S	M	Tu	W	Th	F	Sa

ABBREVIATIONS

M = Monday,   Tu = Tuesday,   W = Wednesday,
Th = Thursday,   F = Friday,   Sa = Saturday,
S = Sunday.

INSTRUCTIONS

1. Locate in Table I the letter which corresponds to the intersection of the row of CENTURIES and the column of the YEARS.
2. Locate this letter in the row of the month of Table II.
3. Follow the column of this letter to the intersection of the row with the given date of the month. The intersection will give the day of the week.

EASTER DATE CALENDAR

III

	00	01	02	03	04	05	06	07	08	09	10	11	12	13	14	15	16	17	18
Years in Centuries	19	20	21	22	23	24	25	26	27	28	29	30	31	32	33	34	35	36	37
	38	39	40	41	42	43	44	45	46	47	48	49	50	51	52	53	54	55	56
	57	58	59	60	61	62	63	64	65	66	67	68	69	70	71	72	73	74	75
	76	77	78	79	80	81	82	83	84	85	86	87	88	89	90	91	92	93	94
	95	96	97	98	99														

New Style Centuries																			
15	2	14	15	16	17	18	19	20	21	22	23	24	25	26	27	28	29	30	1
16	18	19	20	21	22	23	24	25	26	27	28	29	30	1	2	14	15	16	17
17	12	13	14	15	16	17	18	19	20	21	3	4	5	6	7	8	9	10	11
18	17	18	19	20	21	3	4	5	6	7	8	9	10	11	12	13	14	15	16
19	22	23	24	25	26	27	28	29	30	1	2	3	4	5	6	7	8	9	10
20	27	28	29	30	1	2	3	4	5	6	7	19	9	10	22	23	24	25	26
21	2	3	4	5	6	7	19	9	10	22	23	24	25	26	27	28	29	30	1

INSTRUCTIONS

1. In Table I of the Perpetual Calendar obtain the letter which is located at the intersection of the Column of the Years in Centuries with the Row of New Style Centuries.
2. In Table III of the Easter Date Calendar obtain the number which is located at the intersection of the Column of the Years in Centuries with the Row of the New Style Centuries.
3. In Table IV of the Easter Date Calendar obtain the number which is located at the intersection of the letter obtained in 1 above with the column of the row of the number obtained in 2 above. This number is the Easter Date.
4. The italic numbers refer to the month of March. The numbers printed in roman type give April dates.

IV

	a	b	c	d	e	f	g
1	6	12	11	10	9	8	7
2	30	29	28	27	26	1	31
3	20	19	18	17	16	15	14
4	6	5	4	3	9	8	7
5	23	29	28	27	26	25	24
6	13	12	11	17	16	15	14
7	6	5	4	3	2	1	31
8	20	19	18	24	23	22	21
9	13	12	11	10	9	8	14
10	30	29	28	3	2	1	31
11	20	19	18	17	16	22	21
12	6	5	11	10	9	8	7
13	30	29	28	27	26	25	31
14	13	19	18	17	16	15	14
15	6	5	11	10	9	8	7
16	23	22	28	27	26	25	24
17	13	12	11	10	16	15	14
18	30	5	4	3	2	1	31
19	20	19	18	24	23	22	21
20	13	12	11	10	9	8	7
21	30	29	28	27	2	1	31
22	20	19	18	17	16	15	21
23	6	5	4	10	9	8	7
24	30	29	28	27	26	25	24
25	13	12	18	17	16	15	14
26	6	5	4	3	2	1	7
27	20	19	18	24	23	22	21
28	13	12	11	10	9	15	14
29	30	29	4	3	2	1	31
30	20	19	18	17	23	22	21

year 1954 is determined as follows. In Table I of the Perpetual Calendar we find that the intersection of the column headed "54" with the row marked "19" yields the letter "c." In Table III of the Easter Date Calendar we locate the intersection of the column "54" with the row "19." This intersection yields the number 8. With the letter "c" and the number 8 we refer to Table IV of the Easter Date Calendar; the intersection gives the date, April 18.

Chapter 9

ONE-WAY GEOMETRY

The Hungry Fly

Whether insects are endowed with intelligence is not for mathematicians to decide. But one special fly has demonstrated a knowledge of a certain type of geometry which is not even studied in high schools.

In a certain mathematical laboratory a model of a geometric solid (as illustrated in Figure 26) was constructed. The model was made of various pieces of cardboard which

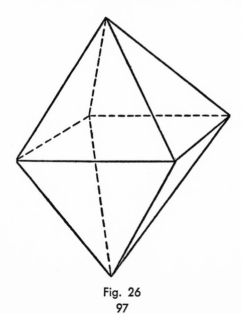

Fig. 26

were glued together. A hungry fly discovered the freshly made model, and it made a bee-line (or fly-line) for it, especially for the glue. It attacked the glue with great diligence; having eaten all the glue on one edge, it traveled immediately to the next. It confined its travels to the edges, and, being an economical fly, it never traveled along an edge twice. All the facts concerning the behavior of the fly were duly noted and a record of its travels is shown in Figure 27.

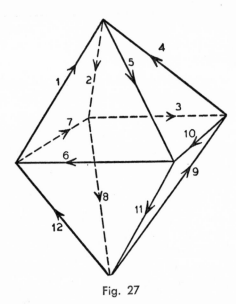

Fig. 27

This hungry fly never went to school and certainly never studied geometry or read a geometry book. It is extremely doubtful that this fly, if it had had an opportunity to land on a page of a geometry book, could have gathered the information required for the performance of this feat. But, still, the fly displayed a knowledge of certain geometric properties which are never mentioned in geometry schoolbooks. The ways of nature are mysterious. Animals and insects often display behavior which poses real mathematical problems.

Odd or Even Again

Let us examine the drawing shown in Figure 26. We note that this drawing represents a geometric solid figure which has eight faces, each an equilateral triangle (a triangle all of whose sides are equal). It has twelve edges. It also has six vertices, and each vertex has four edges converging at it. The solid geometric figure is known as a *regular octahedron*. The qualifying adjective "regular" refers to the fact that this solid geometric figure is composed of one kind of face, and that all of its edges are equal in length.

The clue to the fly's travels lies in the fact that at each vertex of the octahedron there are four converging edges. The number *four* is an even number and, therefore, is divisible by 2.

If the number of the edges which converge at every vertex of a geometric solid figure is even, then it is possible to travel along all the edges of the figure by traversing each edge only once.

The reason for this rule is simple. Once a vertex is reached via one route one must move away from the vertex by another route. Thus, a pair of edges is required every time so that the vertex does not become a *dead end*. This means that, when a third edge leads to the same vertex, a fourth edge will permit us to move away from it. Otherwise, we are either "stuck" on that vertex or must travel along an edge which was used previously. If there were a solid with one vertex at which an odd number of vertices converged, while at all other vertices an even number of edges converged, the requirement would not be fulfilled.

It would be possible to select the routes so the last edge would be traversed *last,* and thus the requirements could be fulfilled. Or, one could begin at the vertex with the odd number of edges. Such a solution would be possible if there were solid geometric figures in which all the vertices, but a single one, have an even number of edges, while the single vertex has an odd number of edges. Unfortunately, *such geometric solid figures are impossible*. However, if a solid geometric figure has two vertices with an odd number of edges, the requirements for travel along the edges of the figure could be fulfilled. Such solid geometric figures are possible.

Every edge of a solid geometric figure connects two vertices. If an odd number of edges meet at a vertex, the odd (extra) edge must be connected with another vertex which also has an odd (extra) edge. The odd vertices must, then, come in pairs. There may be two, or four, or six vertices with an odd number of edges, but there can never be one, three, five, or seven such vertices.

If a solid geometric figure has only two vertices each with an odd number of edges, the requirements for the travel along the edges of the solid figure can be fulfilled (see Figure 27). If, however, there are more than two vertices with an odd number of edges converging at them, these requirements cannot be fulfilled.

The Secret of the Fly's Travels

A solid geometric figure may have any even number of vertices each of them having an odd number of converging edges. However, only a figure with two, and not more than two vertices, each of them containing an odd number of edges, permits the fulfillment of the travel so that each edge is traversed only once.

All the remarks made above concerning solid geometric figures are equally applicable to plane geometric figures. In other words, whenever reference was made to vertices, we may retain the term "vertices" and regard them as points at which lines converge. Whenever reference was made to edges, we may replace the term "edge" by the term *line*. The following illustration shows the method of traversing the lines of a plane geometric figure (see Figure 28). Note that the square in Figure 28a is crossed by a straight line. Thus,

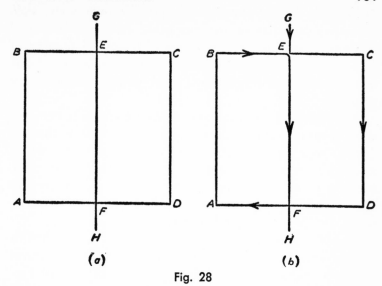

(a)   (b)

Fig. 28

where the straight line crosses the two opposite sides of the square there are vertices with an even number of lines converging at the vertices respectively. In each case there are four converging lines. These are *AF, DF, EF,* and *HF* for the vertex *F,* and *BE, CE, FE,* and *GE* for the vertex *E.* There are four vertices, *A, B, C,* and *D* and two lines converge at each. There are also two vertices, namely *G* and *H.* Each of these vertices has one line, namely, *EG* for the vertex *G* and *FH* for the vertex *H.* Thus, these two vertices are "odd." The solution of the problem is shown in Figure 28*b.* Note that we start with an odd vertex. This is the most important rule of the procedure.

Problems of the type described here are known as *unicursal drawings,* or drawings with one stroke of the pen or pencil so that no part of the drawing is passed over more than once. The rules for the solution of such problems follow:

1. Count all the types of the vertices. Whenever lines intersect they meet in a vertex.

2. The point of intersection of the lines is considered the point from which these lines emanate. Thus, if two lines intersect, they meet in a vertex at which four lines converge.

3. Ascrtain how many vertices with an odd number of lines are in the figure.

4. If there are more than two odd vertices, do not attempt to solve the problem. The solution is impossible.

5. If there are only two odd vertices, start the drawing with one of these, and reserve the other so that the completion of the drawing is made at the second odd vertex.

6. At any rate, during the drawing be certain that the pen or the pencil is moved so that at no time it reaches a vertex which is a "dead end," that is, do not complete the drawing before all the paths are traversed.

7. If there are no vertices with an odd number of converging lines, the drawing may be started from any vertex. A figure with only even vertices can be always drawn unicursally.

The figures shown in Figure 29 cannot be drawn unicursally. Note that each figure has four odd vertices.

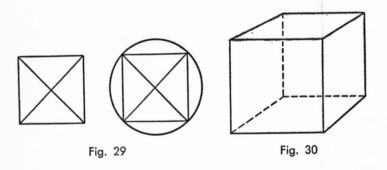

Fig. 29   Fig. 30

The figure shown in Figure 30, a cube, cannot be drawn unicursally. The cube has eight odd vertices.

The figure shown in Figure 31 can be drawn unicursally. All of its vertices are even.

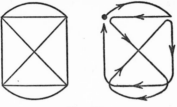

Fig. 31

The figure shown in Figure 32 can be drawn unicursally. All of its vertices, except two are even. The two odd vertices are *A* and *B*.

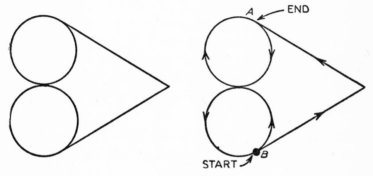

Fig. 32

The figures shown in Figure 33 cannot be drawn unicursally.

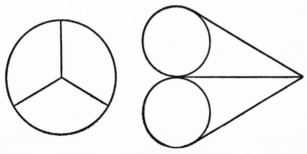

Fig. 33

The following problems are offered to the reader as exercises. After the reader has mastered them, he might try his hand at drawing his own designs and try them on his friends.

PROBLEMS

1. Figure 34.

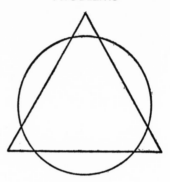

Fig. 34

2. Figure 35.

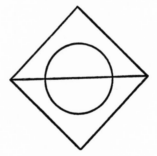

Fig. 35

3. Figure 36.

Fig. 36

4. Figure 37.

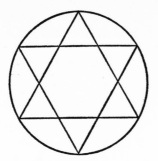

Fig. 37

5. Figure 38.

Fig. 38

6. Figure 39.

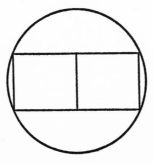

Fig. 39

7. Figure 40.

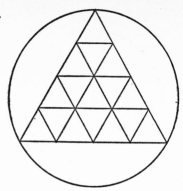

Fig. 40

8. Figure 41.

Fig. 41

9. Figure 42.

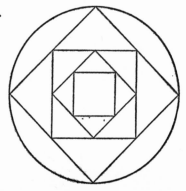

Fig. 42

10. Figure 43.

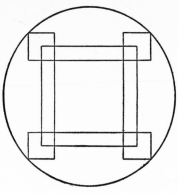

Fig. 43

11. Figure 44.

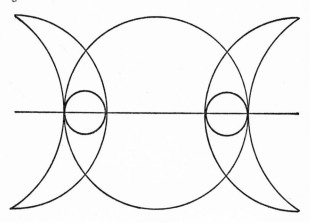

Fig. 44

12. Figure 45.

Fig. 45

Chapter 10

THE CIRCLE-SQUARERS' PARADISE

The Impossible Does Not Take a Little Longer

During World War II the United States Navy organized a special construction corps whose men adapted the motto "The difficult we do now, the impossible takes a little longer." And the men of this corps, known as the Sea Bees (from the phonetics of the initials of the words "Construction Battalions") really performed wonders. They tackled construction assignments which, under any ordinary conditions and circumstances, would have been considered "impossible." Their record stands unblemished.

Luckily, for the record of the Sea Bees, they were never asked to construct a straight line equal in length to the circumference of a circle or to construct a square whose area would be equal to the area of a circle. If such an assignment had been made, the Sea Bees would have failed and failed miserably.

The construction of a straight line equal to the circumference of a circle or a square whose area is equal to the area of a circle is usually limited to the so-called classical constructions. Classical constructions require that only compasses and unmarked straightedges (used for drawing straight lines) be employed. All other instruments are prohibited. This limitation on instruments is directly associated with the fact that in the Elementary Geometry of Euclid (the one studied in high schools) only compasses and unmarked straightedges are employed.

For more than two thousand years, that is, since Euclid published his work on Geometry (known as *The Elements*), people have attempted to solve the problem of the *quadrature of the circle* (this is the name mathematicians assigned to the "area of the circle" problem described above). No matter how hard men tried, no matter how ingenious the attempts, the problem defied all the efforts at solution. Some of these men spent their lifetimes trying to solve this problem. Many of them carried their hopes to their graves.

In 1873, a German mathematician, F. Lindemann, finally proved that determining the quadrature of the circle by means of compasses and a straightedge was impossible. He proved that the numerical value of the ratio of the length of the circumference of a circle to the length of the diameter of this same circle cannot be computed exactly, and hence that a straight line segment equal to the length of the circumference of a circle cannot be constructed when its diameter is taken as a unit of measure. Men, especially those who are not versed in mathematics, still try and try hard to do that which is now definitely known as *impossible*. Rarely a year passes but someone announces he has solved the problem. Usually such announcements are accompanied by claims that the solution is perfect, that it must be kept secret, that the "discoverer of the solution" would be willing to reveal it if he were paid a handsome sum for his secret. If there is a gullible man who is ready to fall for such an announcement, he might more profitably invest his savings in the Spanish Inheritance scheme. Those who try to solve the problem of the quadrature of the circle by means of compasses and a straightedge, live in a Circle-Squarers' Paradise.

The Pi That Is Never Quite Done

The ratio of the length of the circumference of a circle to the length of its diameter is denoted symbolically by the Greek letter π.

If the symbol C denotes the length of the circumference of a circle, and if the symbol D denotes the length of the diameter of this circle, then the relation between π, C and D is stated as

$$\frac{C}{D} = \pi \quad \text{or} \quad \pi \cdot D = C$$

The symbolic expression $\pi \cdot D = C$ may be also stated in terms of the radius of the circle. Since the diameter of the circle is twice as long as the radius, that is, $D = 2r$ (the symbol r denotes the radius of the circle), then $C = 2\pi r$. The area of a circle, in terms of the diameter and the radius respectively, is stated symbolically as $A = \dfrac{\pi D^2}{4}$ or $A = \pi r^2$, where the symbol A denotes the value of the area of the circle.

The numerical value of π, as indicated above, cannot be calculated exactly. The best one can ever expect to do is to obtain the value approximately. Mathematicians have devised various means for calculating the value of π. This value was given in the Bible as 3. The Egyptians used 3.16 * for its value. Archimedes suggested the value of $3\frac{1}{7}$ which is approximately equal to 3.142857. The Greek mathematician Heron mentions that Archimedes also suggested that the numerical value of π lies somewhere between $\frac{211,882}{67,441}$ and $\frac{195,882}{62,351}$, that is, between 3.1415904 . . . and 3.1416016. . . . The Romans employed the value of 3.125 (in their statement its value was $3\frac{1}{8}$). The Hindus as well as the Greek mathematician Ptolemy used the value of $\frac{355}{113}$ which is approximately equal to 3.1415929. . . .

In 1873, the mathematician Shanks computed the value of π to the first 707 decimal places. In 1946, this approximate value was extended by Ferguson at Manchester University (England) to 808 decimal places. This same recomputation was done by Wrench (in Washington, D. C.). Their results

* They employed the approximate value of $(\frac{16}{9})^2$ which is approximately 3.16049.

uncovered a mistake in Shanks' calculations. Shanks' value is incorrect, starting with the 528th decimal. Modern electronic computers should offer no difficulty in extending the approximate value of π to many more decimal places. However, such calculations may be carried on from here to eternity and beyond, and the end will never be reached. The approximate value of π with the first 35 decimal places is
$\pi = 3.14159265358979323846264338327950288....$ Such a value is only a curiosity. Practically, so many decimal places are not needed for any sort of computation.

The numerical value of π is often given in verse form, where the successive digits in the numerical value are represented by the number of letters in each word. Following are some of these verses:

   3 1 4 1   6
A. Yes, I have a number.

   3 1 4 1 5   9   2 6   5
B. How I wish I could recollect of circle round
   3   5   8   9   7
   The exact relation Archimede unwound.

   3 1 4 1 5   9
C. Sir, I send a rhyme excelling
   2 6   5   3   5   8
   In sacred truth and rigid spelling;
    9   7   9
   Numerical sprites elucidate
   3 2 3   8   4   6
   For me the lexicon's dull weight
   2 6   4
   If Nature gain
   3 3   8
   Not you complain
   3 2 7   9
   Tho' Dr. Johnson fulminate.

    3 1   4   1 5   9
D. Now I know a spell unfailing
    2 6   5   3 5   8
An artful charm, for tasks availing,
    9   7   9
Intricate results entailing,
    3 2 3   8   4
Not in too exacting mood,
    6   2 6   4
Poetry is pretty good,
    3 3   8   3 2
Try the talisman. Let be
    7   9
Adverse ingenuity.

Similar verses have been composed in many other languages.

Assorted Recipes for Pi

The calculation of the numerical value of π (all such values can be obtained approximately) has occupied the attention of mathematicians for a long time. Many and different formulas have been devised for such calculations. Some of these formulas are given below:

$$\frac{\pi}{4} = 1 - \frac{1}{3} + \frac{1}{5} - \frac{1}{7} + \frac{1}{9} - \frac{1}{11} + \frac{1}{13} - \frac{1}{15} + \cdots$$

$$\frac{\pi}{2} = \frac{2}{1} \cdot \frac{2}{3} \cdot \frac{4}{3} \cdot \frac{4}{5} \cdot \frac{6}{5} \cdot \frac{6}{7} \cdot \frac{8}{7} \cdot \frac{8}{9} \cdot \frac{10}{9} \cdot \frac{10}{11} \cdots$$

$$\frac{\pi}{6} = \frac{\sqrt{3}}{3} \left(1 - \frac{1}{3 \cdot 3} + \frac{1}{3^2 \cdot 5} - \frac{1}{3^3 \cdot 7} + \frac{1}{3^4 \cdot 9} - \frac{1}{3^5 \cdot 11} + \cdots \right)$$

Should one forget the numerical value of π (with a few decimals only) the following calculations will give this value. The approximate value of $\sqrt{2}$ is 1.41421 . . . , and the approximate value of $\sqrt{3}$ is 1.73205. . . . The following relations of the numerical values of $\sqrt{2}$ and $\sqrt{3}$ lead to some very interesting results.

$$(\sqrt{3} + \sqrt{2})(\sqrt{3} - \sqrt{2}) = 3 + \sqrt{6} - \sqrt{6} + 2 = 1$$

But

$$\sqrt{3} + \sqrt{2} = 1.73205 + 1.41421 = 3.14626, \text{ approximately.}$$

Thus, $\sqrt{3} + \sqrt{2} = \pi$, correct to three decimal places.

Then
$$\sqrt{3} - \sqrt{2} = \frac{1}{\sqrt{3} + \sqrt{2}} = \frac{1}{\pi}.$$

Also,

$$\sqrt{3} - \sqrt{2} = 1.73205 - 1.41421 = 0.31384, \text{ approximately.}$$

Thus, $\sqrt{3} + \sqrt{2}$ gives the numerical value of π correct to three decimal places, or four significant digits, while $\sqrt{3} - \sqrt{2}$ gives the numerical value of $1/\pi$ correct to three decimal places, or four significant digits also.

Here the reader should keep in mind an algebraic property regarding the values a and b. This property indicates that

$$(a + b)(a - b) = a^2 - b^2$$

There are many other pairs of square roots whose approximate numerical values will lead to the approximate numerical value of π. Here are some pairs of square roots whose differences give numerical values of π correct to two decimal places (or three significant digits): $\sqrt{15} - \sqrt{3}$; $\sqrt{50} - \sqrt{40}$; $\sqrt{79} - \sqrt{33}$; $\sqrt{196} - \sqrt{118}$. No doubt, there are other pairs of such square roots. If the reader cares to leaf through a table of square roots for an evening or two, he may discover many other pairs.

An equation in which the unknown appears squared is called a *quadratic equation*. In the most general form, a quadratic equation with x as the unknown is written $ax^2 + bx + c = 0$. Those values of the unknown x which, when substituted into the expression $ax^2 + bx + c = 0$, render the calculated value of this expression equal to zero, are known as the roots of the quadratic equation. For example, the equation $x^2 - 5x - 6 = 0$ has two roots, namely, 6 or -1. If we substitute the value of 6 in this equation, we obtain $36 - 30 - 6 = 0$. If we substitute the value of -1 in the same equation, we obtain $1 + 5 - 6 = 0$.

If a quadratic equation has two roots r_1 and r_2, we can obtain the equation by writing $(x - r_1)(x - r_2) = 0$. Performing the indicated multiplication we obtain:

$$x - (r_1 + r_2)x + r_1r_2 = 0$$

If we assume that $(\sqrt{3} + \sqrt{2})$ and $(\sqrt{3} - \sqrt{2})$ are roots of a quadratic equation, we can write the equation. In other words, $\sqrt{3} + \sqrt{2} = r_1$ and $\sqrt{3} - \sqrt{2} = r_2$. Then $r_1 + r_2 = 2\sqrt{3}$, and $r_1r_2 = 1$. We have then the quadratic equation

$$x^2 - 2\sqrt{3}x + 1 = 0$$

Its roots are π or $1/\pi$, whose numerical values are correct to three decimals (or to four significant digits). If we assume that $-(\sqrt{3} + \sqrt{2}) = r_1$ and $-(\sqrt{3} - \sqrt{2}) = r_2$, then we obtain the quadratic equation

$$x^2 + 2\sqrt{3}x + 1 = 0$$

The roots of this quadratic equation are $-\pi$ or $-1/\pi$, whose numerical values are correct to three decimals (or to four significant digits).

If we obtain the product of the two quadratic equations above, that is,

$$(x^2 - 2\sqrt{3}x + 1)(x^2 + 2\sqrt{3}x + 1) = 0$$

we have $$x^4 - 10x^2 + 1 = 0$$

This is an equation in the fourth degree, also known as the bi-quadratic equation. Its roots are: π, $-\pi$, $1/\pi$, or $-1/\pi$, all of whose values are correct to three decimals (or to four significant digits).

The quadratic equation $x^2 + 8x - 35 = 0$ has a positive root

$$x = -4 + \sqrt{51} = 3.141428 \text{ approximately}$$

This root differs from the numerical value of π, starting with the fourth decimal, by approximately 0.000165.

The quadratic equation $64x^2 - 160x - 129 = 0$ has a positive root which differs from the approximate value of π by less than one ten-millionth. The reader may check the values of the roots of the two quadratic equations by solving the equations. The formula for the root of a quadratic equation is

$$x_{1,2} = \frac{-b \pm \sqrt{b^2 - 4ac}}{2a}$$

where the symbols a, b, and c are the two coefficients of the unknown x and the free term respectively.

The Circle Rectified . . . Approximately

The construction of a straight line segment which is *approximately* equal to the length of the circumference of a circle, provided only a compass and an unmarked straightedge are used, may be performed in many and diverse ways. Some such constructions are complicated, while others are comparatively simple. The few examples given below are only representative of a great number of such methods. The reader who wishes to consult the extensive literature on this subject is referred to the books (most of them in German) listed below.

F. Rudio. *Archimedes, Huygens, Lambert, Legendre. Vier Abhandlungen über die Kreismessung.* Leipzig, 1892.

H. Schubert. *Die Quadratur des Kreises in berufenen und unberufene Köpfen.* Hamburg, 1899.

E. Beutel. *Die Quadratur des Kreises.* Leipzig, 1920.

Th. Vahlen. *Konstruktionen und Approximationen.* Leipzig, 1911.

The property of the approximation $\sqrt{3} + \sqrt{2} = \pi$ may be employed in the construction of a straight line segment equal (approximately) to the length of the circumference of a circle. This is also known as the *rectification* of the *circle*. The construction is obtained as follows (see Figure 46).

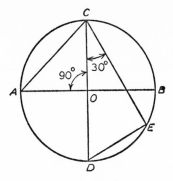

Fig. 46

Draw the two perpendicular diameters AB and CD of the circle. From the point D mark off with the radius of the circle the point E on the circumference of the circle. Join the points A and C. Also join the points C and E. Then $AC = \sqrt{2}R$ and $CE = \sqrt{3}R$, where R represents the radius of the circle. The sum of the straight line segments $2AC$ and $2CE$ will be approximately equal to the length of the circumference of the circle, correct to three decimals (or to four significant digits).

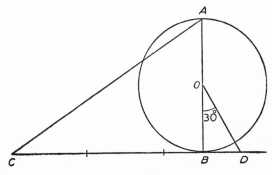

Fig. 47

Another approximate construction of the length of the circumference of a circle may be obtained as follows (see Figure 47).

Draw the diameter AB of the circle. At point B draw the tangent BC whose length is equal to $3R$ diminished by one third of the length of the side of an equilateral triangle inscribed in the circle. The length of the side of an equilateral triangle inscribed in the circle is equal to $R\sqrt{3}$. Thus,

$$BC = DC - DB, \text{ where } DB = \frac{R\sqrt{3}}{3}, \text{ and}$$

$$BC = 3R - \frac{R\sqrt{3}}{3}$$

Join the points A and C. Then from the right triangle ABC, by means of the Pythagorean relation $AC^2 = AB^2 + BC^2$, we have, since $AB = 2R$, that

$$AC^2 = 4R^2 + R^2\left(3 - \frac{\sqrt{3}}{3}\right)^2$$

or $AC^2 = R^2(13.333333 - 3.464102)^2$

Finally, $AC = R\sqrt{9.869231} = 3.14153R$ approximately

The length of the circumference of the circle (approximately) is equal to the length of the straight line segment $2AC$.

Chapter II

ROLLING CIRCLES
AND AIRPLANES

Don't Let Your Reasoning Deceive You

Very often, conclusions reached by reasoning do not correspond to the actual facts. Even such a great intellect as Aristotle was deceived when he applied reasoning to such things as whether heavier stones fall more rapidly than lighter ones. Aristotle's theory that heavier objects fall faster than lighter ones prevailed for many years. Then Galileo, by

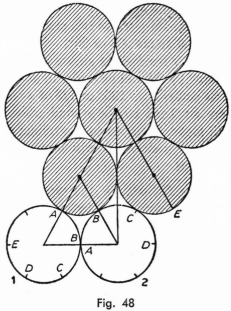

Fig. 48

the method of experiment, showed the fallibility of reasoning without resort to experimentation and proved that all bodies fall at the same speed. So much for a classical example.

Suppose someone asked you to place 8 pennies on a table in a manner shown in Figure 48. The eighth coin, indicated by the unshaded circle, is to be rolled around the other six *without permitting it to slide*. (As you can see in the diagram the seventh, or inner, coin cannot be touched.)

Now, you are asked: "How many turns will the moving coin make before it returns to its original position?" Let us, like Aristotle, "reason this problem out." After all, the situation is quite simple. All that we have to do is to examine the drawing, note the principal facts concerning this problem, and then we can make a prediction. We note the following facts:

1. As the rolling circle moves along its path it turns through some angles. Thus, when the rolling circle is in position 2, it has moved forward through the arc *AB* which contains 60°.
2. Each of the fixed circles has two arcs which correspond to an arc equal to arc *AB* or 60°.
3. Thus, for every fixed circle an arc of 120° is required to be covered by the rolling circle. In other words, each fixed circle contributes 120° or 1/3 of a complete turn.
4. There are six fixed circles around which the rolling circle will move. Thus, when the rolling circle returns to its original position, it will have made $6 \cdot \frac{1}{3} = 2$ complete turns.

Now, let us, like Galileo, use the experimental method. We will keep a very close watch over the number of turns which *actually* take place. To our amazement close observation contradicts our prediction. The rolling circle makes *four* complete turns between the initial and the final position. Our reasoning must have gone astray somewhere. We repeat the experiment. The result is the same. Four turns and not two. What was wrong with our reasoning?

If a circle rolls along a straight line and it covers a distance which is equal to the length of 1/3 of the circumferences of the rolling circle, then this rolling circle covers the distance equal to 1/3 of the length of its circumference. In other words, it makes a 1/3 turn.

If a rolling circle does not move along a straight line, but it rolls along an arc of some curved line (it may be an arc of a circle), the situation is quite different. In our experiment the rolling circle moves along an arc which is equal to 1/3 of the length of its circumference. Under such circumstances it makes more than 1/3 of a turn. This may be noted if we carefully examine the drawing in Figure 48.

As the moving circle rolls along the fixed circles it makes more than 1/3 turn between the position when the point A touches a fixed circle (circle number 1) and the position when the point E touches a fixed circle (circle number 2). Actually, the rolling circle makes a turn through 240°, that is, it makes 2/3 of a turn. Since there are six circles which have to be touched by the rolling circle, the total number of turns which the rolling circle must complete is

$$6 \cdot \frac{2}{3} = 4$$

A rolling circle makes more turns when it follows a curved path or a series of connected lines with changing directions than it does when it follows a straight line of equal length.

Suppose that the moving circle rolls, without sliding, along the perimeter of a square whose sides are equal to the length of the circumference of the circle. Thus, when the rolling circle covers the distance AB it makes one turn. But at the vertex B the rolling circle must make a turn so that it will become tangent to the side BC. This turn will be equal to the external angle which is denoted by the symbol a.

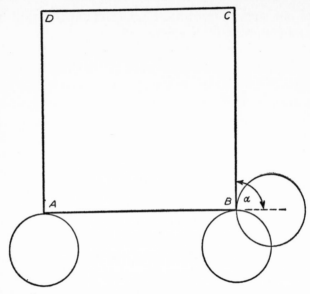

Fig. 49

A complete turn, or 360°, is also denoted by the symbol 2π. The sum of the external angles of any closed polygon is equal to 360° or to 2π. If the polygon is regular, that is, all of its sides are equal and all of its internal angles are equal, then all of its external angles are also equal. If a regular polygon consists of n sides, then each external angle is equal to $360°/n$ or to $2\pi/n$.

Let a rolling circle make a turn of an angle α. This turn represents that part of a complete turn as the angle α is a part of 2π. In other words, at each vertex of the square, the rolling circle makes a turn which is equal to $\alpha/2\pi$ turns. But in the case of a square α is equal to $2\pi/4$ or $\pi/2$. If we substitute the value of α in the expression $\alpha/2\pi$, we learn that the rolling circle makes 1/4 of a turn at each vertex. Thus, while going through all the four vertices of a square, the rolling circle will make 1 complete turn in addition to the turns it will make while it rolls along the sides of the square. Since the circle makes one complete turn on each side of our square, the total number of turns it will make while rolling around the square will be 5.

Now, let us assume that the number of the sides of the regular polygon is doubled, while each of the sides is still equal in length to the length of the circumference of the rolling circle. Each of the external angles of the polygon of eight sides is $2\pi/8$, while the amount of turn at each vertex is equal to $\alpha/2\pi$ of a complete turn. Substituting the value of α in the expression $\alpha/2\pi$ indicates that the rolling circle will make 1/8 of a turn at each vertex. As the rolling circle completes its passage through all the eight vertices it will make an additional complete turn.

If the number of the sides of the regular polygon is doubled again, the same result will be obtained. The external angle at each vertex will be equal to $\alpha = 2\pi/16$, and the turn at each vertex will be equal to $\alpha/2\pi$ of a complete turn. This means that at each vertex the rolling circle will make 1/16 of a complete turn, and, after passing through all the 16 vertices, the rolling circle will complete one additional turn.

Suppose that doubling the number of the sides of the polygon is continued indefinitely. In the limiting situation the polygon should reach the circumference of a circle in which it may be inscribed. The rolling circle, after passing through an infinite number of vertices, will complete only one additional turn. Now, suppose that the circle around which the rolling circle moves has a circumference equal to the circumference of the rolling circle. Then, while the rolling circle moves around such a circle, it will make the following turns:

1. It will make one turn that will correspond to the length of its circumference which is also equal to the circumference of the circle around which it moves.
2. It will make an additional turn that corresponds to the going through an infinite number of vertices.

Thus, while rolling along a circle equal to itself, a circle will make two complete turns between the starting point and its return to that point.

This discussion indicates that the circle which is rolling along the six fixed circles (with the seventh in the center) should have been expected to make the four turns actually observed.

PROBLEMS

1. A circle rolls (without sliding) along the sides of an equilateral triangle. Each side of this triangle is equal in length to the length of the circumference of the circle. How many turns will this circle complete upon return to its starting point?

2. A circle rolls (without sliding) along the sides of a regular pentagon. Each side of the pentagon is equal in length to one half the length of the circumference of the circle. How many turns will this circle complete upon its return to the starting point?

3. A circle rolls (without sliding) along the circumference of a circle whose diameter is twice the diameter of the rolling circle. How many turns will the rolling circle complete upon its return to its starting point?

4. A circle rolls (without sliding) along the circumference of a circle whose diameter is one half the diameter of the rolling circle. How many turns will the rolling circle complete upon its return to the starting point?

A Straight Line Without a Straightedge

When a circle rolls (without sliding) along the edge of a figure, some very interesting facts may be observed by watching a single point on that circle. Let us imagine that at some point on the circumference of the rolling circle there is a special inking gadget which does not cause friction and which is so constructed that it has a tracing point (something akin to a pen) which is fed ink from a special container. Suppose that the circle rolls (without sliding) along a straight line. This is illustrated in Figure 50. If A_1 is the starting point of our observations, the rolling circle will be

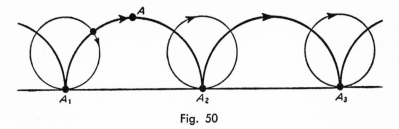

Fig. 50

in position A_1 when the inking point is also in that position. As soon as the circle starts out on its rolling motion this inking point begins to trace out its path. When the rolling circle moves through a distance which is equal to the length of its circumference, the inking point arrives at the point A_2. As the circle continues to roll along the straight line, the inking point continues to trace out its path. The curve so traced is known as the *cycloid*. Every time the circle rolls through a distance equal to the length of its circumference the inking point returns to the straight line.

Suppose that the rolling circle is placed within another

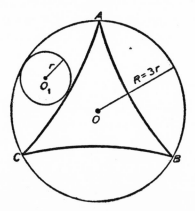

Fig. 51

circle whose radius is three times as long as the radius of
the rolling circle (see Figure 51). The circumference of the
circle within which the smaller circle rolls is $2\pi R$, as is
the circumference of the rolling circle. But since $R = 3r$, the
circumference of the larger circle is $2\pi \cdot 3r$ or $6\pi r$. Thus the
circumference of the large circle is three times as large as
the circumference of the small circle. The inking gadget will
touch the circumference of the large circle three times as
the small circle moves around the larger one. The curve
which the inking point traces out is called the *hypocycloid*.
In this case, when $R = 3r$, the hypocycloid consists of three
identical parts which come to a point, two at a time. This
point is known as a *cusp*. Thus, when $R = 3r$, the hypocycloid has three cusps.

If the circle, within which the rolling circle moves, has a
radius four times as long as the radius of the smaller circle
$(R = 4r)$, the circumference of the larger circle will equal
$2\pi R$ and the circumference of the rolling circle will equal
$2\pi r$. The circumference of the larger circle, when stated in
terms of the radius of the smaller circle, will be $2\pi \cdot 4r$ or
$8\pi r$. The inking gadget will touch the circumference of the
larger circle four times as the small circle moves inside the
large circle. This is shown in Figure 52. The curve which
the inking point will trace out is a hypocycloid with four
cusps.

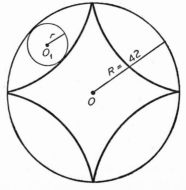

Fig. 52

Should the radius of the large circle be 5 times as large as the radius of the rolling circle, the inking point, which is attached to the small circle rolling inside the large circle, will trace out a hypocycloid with five cusps. Finally, we may generalize that if the relation between the two radii is $R = nr$, where n is any whole number (integer), then the inking point, which is attached to the small circle rolling inside the large circle, will trace out a hypocycloid with n cusps.

If $n = 2$, the relation between the two radii is $R = 2r$, and we should have a hypocycloid with two cusps. Let us examine this case in detail. Figure 53 represents the drawing of such a situation.

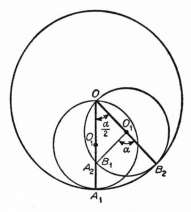

Fig. 53

As the small circle rolls (without sliding) inside the larger circle, one point of the circumference of the small circle always passes through the center O of the large circle. This is due to the fact that the diameter of the small circle is equal to the radius of the large circle.

Suppose that in the initial position A_1 is the point with the inking pen, and this point touches the circumference of the large circle. When the small circle rolls through an angle α, it will touch the large circle in the point B_2. In other words, the small circle rolled along an arc $\alpha/2$ of the large circle. If the radius OA_1 is drawn, then the small circle, in its second position, will intersect the radius OA_1 at point A_2 (which is also denoted by the letter B_1).

The radius of the large circle is R and the radius of the small circle is r. Furthermore, $R = 2r$. If the arc A_1B_2 of the large circle is $\alpha/2$, then the angle A_1OB_2 is measured by this arc; in other words $\angle A_1OB_2$, and the length of the arc A_1B_2 are equal to $R \cdot \alpha/2$ or $2r \cdot \alpha/2$ or $r \cdot \alpha$. On the other hand, the angle A_2OB_2 (which may also be read as B_1OB_2) is inscribed in the small circle. $\angle A_2OB_2$ is identical with $\angle A_1OB_2$, and, therefore $\angle A_2OB_2 = \alpha/2$. But an angle inscribed in a circle is measured by one half of the arc it subtends. Thus, the arc A_2B_2 (which is also denoted as B_1B_2) of the small circle is equal to α, and the length of the arc A_2B_2 is equal to $r \cdot \alpha$. Since the length of the arc A_1B_2 is also equal to $r \cdot \alpha$, we know that the length of the arc A_1B_2 of the large circle is also equal to the length of the arc A_2B_2 of the small circle.

The fact that the two arcs A_1B_2 of the large circle and A_2B_2 of the small circle are equal and that these two arcs are associated with the distance through which the small circle traversed leads us to a very important result. Although the small circle traversed through some distance, the point A_1 (that is, the point which indicated the initial position of the small circle when the latter touched the large circle) moved from the position A_1 to the position A_2 along the radius OA_1. In other words, while the small circle moves along the large circle, when the radii of the large circle and the small circle have the relation $R = 2r$, the initial point A_1 of the small circle moves along the diameter of the large circle which passes through the initial position A_1.

Thus, when the radius of the large circle is twice as large as the radius of the small circle which rolls along the interior circumference of the large circle, any selected point of the small circle describes a straight line and not a hypocycloid with two cusps. Such a hypocycloid is impossible.

The instrument for the drawing of a straight line by means of a rolling circle described above is one of the many instruments in this and other fields which were designed and invented by the Russian mathematician, P. L. Tschebyscheff (1821–1894).

The Path of an Airplane

Since the first airplane flight at Kittyhawk, when a few seconds of air travel demonstrated the practicability of heavier-than-air craft so much progress has been made that a continuous flight of 24 or 48 hours does not even rate front-page news. Man-made machines have conquered undreamed of expanses and distances. Although a visit to the North or South Pole was a daring adventure several decades ago, a flight over either of these Poles is now considered a routine matter. Regular passenger flights from one continent to another across the North Pole are being inaugurated not for reasons of adventure but to save time and distance.

Travel along the surface of the earth is ordinarily planned so that the shortest possible route will be traversed. The surface of the earth is usually assumed to be spherical. The shortest route along the surface of a sphere is taken along a great circle, that is, one which would cut the surface of the sphere into two equal hemispheres. If the route is planned across a Pole, it is taken along one of the great circles which are called meridians.

Let us digress for a few moments and consider the motion of an airplane along a meridian. The motion of an airplane along any other great circle is similar, but a meridian is selected to simplify the discussion. We live on the surface of the earth, and, although we are, to some extent, conscious of the rotation of the earth on its axis, we disregard this motion when the motions of objects on the surface of the earth (or in the air which surrounds the earth) are being considered. We always consider the motion of the object in relation to the surface of the earth rather than in relation to the rotational motion of the earth, because everything participates in this rotational motion.

The fact that the objects which move along the surface of the earth (or in the air surrounding the earth) participate in the rotational motion of the earth must necessarily lead to the following conclusion. The paths of such moving objects, when considered in relation not to the earth but to some imaginary observer who is free from the earth, must appear different. In other words, let us suppose that an observer is located in space and therefore does not participate in the rotatory motion of the earth. Let us suppose also that he is endowed with extremely powerful eyesight. Such an observer would be able to plot the path of an airplane which travels along a meridian over the North Pole. However, we do not need to transport ourselves into the outer space for this purpose, nor do we need to divest ourselves from the gravitational influences of the earth. This experiment can be performed mathematically.

If viewed from above the North Pole, the surface of the earth might appear to us, when projected onto a plane, as a rotating disk. The meridians would appear as diameters of concentric circles. All these meridians will intersect at the common center of these concentric circles, and the point of intersection will represent our North Pole. This rotating disk will complete one revolution in 24 hours. In other words, a given point on the disk will return to its original position after an interval of 24 hours. This disk is shown in Figure 54.

If an airplane starts out from some position on a meridian, say A, and proceeds to travel along a meridian, and if the earth were not rotating on its axis, then the plane's path would appear to the observer as a straight line. This plane would continue to travel along the meridian from the point A and would reach its destination B never deviating from the straight line path. On the other hand, if the earth is rotating on its axis, this rotational motion must be added

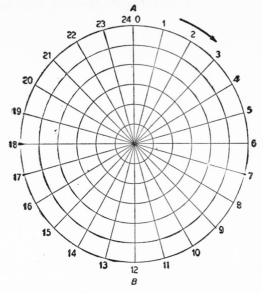

Fig. 54

(not in the sense of arithmetic addition, though) to the forward motion of the airplane. The observer stationed in the outer space would note the rotation of the disk, and he would observe a path of an airplane, and this path would not be a straight line.

The rotating disk is divided into 24 equal parts. Each part represents the distance through which the disk will rotate during one hour. Thus, these parts are marked 0 (and 24), 1, 2, 3, 4, 5, 6, 7, 8, 9, 10, 11, 12, 13, 14, 15, 16, 17, 18, 19, 20, 21, 22, and 23. Furthermore, this disk contains con- centric circles, so that each of the diameters of the disk (they represent the meridians) is divided into 12 equal parts.

The reader can construct a device which will trace out the paths described in the examples below. For this purpose, he will need a piece of circular cardboard on which the disk shown in Figure 54 should be drawn. A cardboard strip should be attached along the meridian 0-12 with a slit in the middle allowing the forward movement of a tracing device (a pencil or a pen). The disk should be allowed to rotate, while the strip is kept stationary. The two motions, that is, the rotation of the disk and the forward motion of the tracing device, should be simultaneous. The combination of these two motions will be traced out on the surface of the disk.

Suppose that an airplane leaves the point A in the direction of the point B so that it passes over the North Pole and reaches B within six hours after departure. The points A and B are equidistant from the North Pole. After one hour the airplane will reach the point a (see Figure 55). But the rotation of the disk will transport the point a to the position a'. After another hour of flight the airplane will reach the point b. But the rotational motion of the disk will transport the point b to the position b'. At the end of the third hour the airplane will be passing over the North Pole. However, while all this takes place, the point B is carried forward, along the rim of the rotating disk. At the end of

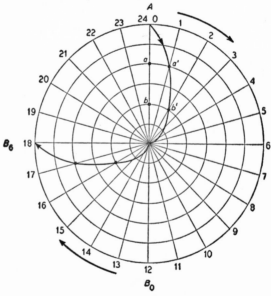

Fig. 55

six hours the point B will be in the position B_6. As the airplane continues on its flight, the tracing instrument continues to trace out the path of the airplane (as observed from the outer space). The curve shown in Figure 55 represents the path of the airplane as it would have been observed from the outer space. The path would appear to be a straight line to an observer on the rotating disk and to an observer on the airplane.

Figure 54 shows the path of an airplane (as observed from outer space) when the distance between the points A and B is covered in 12 hours. That this path suggests that the airplane returns to its point of departure is only an illusion. The rotating disk makes one half of a turn in 12 hours and results in the transposition of the point A to where the point B was 12 hours ago, and the transposition of the point B to where the point A was 12 hours ago.

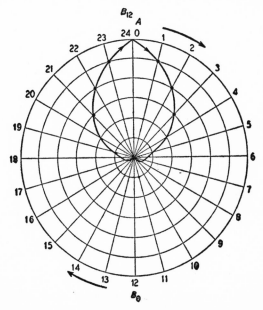

Fig. 56

Figure 57 represents the path of an airplane (as observed from outer space) when the distance between the points A and B is covered in 24 hours. After 24 hours have elapsed, the point B (which is rotating with the disk) will return to its original position. The airplane, that is, its representation by the point A, will pass over the North Pole after 12 hours of flight. The path consists of two equal parts; the second half of the flight is a mirror image of the first half of the flight

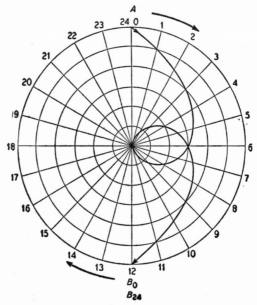

Fig. 57

If the distance between the points A and B is covered in 48 hours, the point B, the destination of the airplane, will make two complete revolutions on the rotating disk. The airplane will pass over the North Pole at the end of 24 hours of flight. The path of the plane will again consist of two equal parts, and the second half of the flight will be a mirror image of the trace of the first half of the flight. This path is shown in Figure 58.

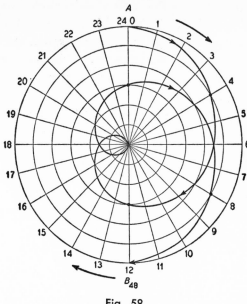

Fig. 58

In our discussion we have not considered other motions of the earth. The earth and the moon revolve around a common point, while the moon revolves around the earth. Furthermore, the earth moves around the sun. And the forward motion of the sun carries the earth, everything on the earth, and everything in the earth's atmosphere along the sun's path. To obtain a reasonably correct trace of the path of an airplane (as observed from the outer space), the motions of the earth and of the sun must be taken into account. This will produce extremely complicated traces. However, we must always remember that the universe in which we live is not a simple organization. Everything that is in this universe belongs to a system and not a star, not a plant, not even a single speck exists or can exist independently of this universe.

PROBLEMS

5. Trace the path of an airplane which covers the distance, while passing over the North Pole, between the points A and B equidistant from the Pole, if time of flight is 9 hours.

6. Trace the path of an airplane which covers the distance, while passing over the North Pole, between the points A and B equidistant from the Pole, if the time of flight is 18 hours.

Chapter 12

TRIGONOMETRY
LOST AND
REGAINED

The Great Disaster

Mankind is currently experiencing many fears. We shall not concern ourselves with the validity of these fears. We are living in the shadow of a new kind of warfare which, if unleashed, threatens the foundations of our civilization. The destructiveness of modern weapons is so powerful that mankind itself may suffer destruction and near annihilation.

An atomic attack, if perpetrated by an unscrupulous enemy, most assuredly will be directed against large concentrations of populations and industry. It will destroy many human beings and will reduce to ashes buildings, factories, schools, and libraries. It is alarming to imagine what would happen to all the records of man's industrial and scientific achievements. Books will probably become nonexistent. Atomic weapons, however nightmarish they may be, are with us. They are a stark reality which we must face squarely.

Suppose that an atomic attack took place, and that it was so widespread that all the books and all other records of civilization were completely destroyed or made useless. Not a single book, page, newspaper, notebook, is left intact. Everything is reduced to ashes so that any restoration has become absolutely impossible. It is a very gloomy and dreary picture. The only thing left is hope. But hope and faith, in combination with human ingenuity, are a formidable force.

One of the victims of an atomic war would be mathematics. All that has been developed, invented, discovered, and created in mathematics would suffer the same fate as that of mankind. All the books on mathematics would disappear, and with this disappearance would go everything which is associated with trigonometry.

Trigonometry is one of the branches of mathematics which is very important from the practical point of view. It is important in the building industry; it is indispensable in measuring distances. On it depend navigation on the seas and in the air. If trigonometry should suddenly disappear, most of the important activities of men would come to a stop. Since trigonometry is also important in warfare, an enemy might profitably aim to strike a death blow at all the trigonometric information that is available to his victim.

But trigonometry would be needed immediately after the enemy had done his work. Man would have to start from scratch and attempt to restore all that had been destroyed. Mankind could not, however, sit and wait while the restoration went on. Something would have to be done to take care of the intervening period. And here is where man's ingenuity would come to the rescue.

The Restoration Begins

For practical purposes, the numerical values of trigonometric functions (the sine, the cosine, the tangent) need not contain too many decimal places (or significant digits). It should be understood that almost none of the numerical values of trigonometric functions can be computed exactly.

The restoration of the trigonometic tables, that is, of the values of the sine, the cosine, and the tangent, would require a minimum of information. All that would be necessary is summarized below:

1. The sine of an angle is defined as the ratio of the numerical values of the side of a right triangle which is

opposite that angle and the hypotenuse of that triangle. Thus, if the triangle ABC (see Figure 59) is a right triangle, then

Fig. 59

$$\frac{BC}{AB} = \sin A \quad \text{and} \quad \frac{AC}{AB} = \sin B$$

2. According to the Pythagorean relation,

$$\sin^2 A + \cos^2 A = 1$$

3. Since the sum of the two acute angles of a right triangle is equal to 90°, and, the definition of the cosine is

$$\frac{AC}{AB} = \cos A \quad \text{and} \quad \frac{BC}{AB} = \cos B$$

$\cos A = \sin B$ and $\cos B = \sin A$, and $\cos A = \sin (90° - A)$, and $\sin A = \cos (90° - A)$.

4. Geometry tells us that the numerical values of the sines of the angles of 30°, 45°, 60° and 90° are

$$\sin 30° = 0.5$$
$$\sin 45° = \sqrt{2}/2 = 0.7071$$
$$\sin 60° = \sqrt{3}/3 = 0.8660$$
$$\sin 90° = 1$$

5. For small angles the numerical value of the sine may be computed as the ratio of the length of the arc of a circle (which corresponds to that angle) and the radius of that circle. Thus, if we have a small angle AOB,

and AB is the length of the arc, while BC is the side of the right triangle OBC, then the two ratios OB/AO and BC/AO do not differ numerically significantly. (See Figure 60.)

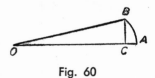

Fig. 60

6. The numerical value of π is taken to be approximately 3.14159. From this information we may proceed with the calculation of the numerical values of the sines and cosines.

The length of the circumference of a circle whose radius is R is $2\pi R$. If R is equal to 1, the length of the circumference of the circle is 2π. Since in the circumference of a circle there are 360°, the length of arc of 1° is:

$$\frac{2\pi}{360} = \frac{3.14159}{180} = 0.01745 \text{ approximately}$$

The length of an arc of 2° is:

$$\frac{2\pi \cdot 2}{360} = \frac{3.14159}{90} = 0.03490 \text{ approximately}$$

The length of an arc of 3° is:

$$\frac{2\pi \cdot 3}{360} = \frac{3.14159}{60} = 0.05236 \text{ approximately}$$

The length of an arc of 4° is:

$$\frac{2\pi \cdot 4}{360} = \frac{3.14159}{45} = 0.06981 \text{ approximately}$$

The length of an arc of 5° is:

$$\frac{2\pi \cdot 5}{360} = \frac{3.14159}{36} = 0.08725 \text{ approximately}$$

Thus, we may tabulate the values of the sines thus far obtained as:

$$\sin 1° = 0.0175$$
$$\sin 2° = 0.0349$$
$$\sin 3° = 0.0524$$
$$\sin 4° = 0.0698$$
$$\sin 5° = 0.0873$$

The calculation of the cosine of the five angles may be performed by means of the relation $\sin^2 A + \cos^2 A = 1$. This leads to the formula $\cos A = \sqrt{1 - \sin^2 A}$ which will be employed for this purpose. The computations give the following values:

$$\cos 1° = 0.9998$$
$$\cos 2° = 0.9994$$
$$\cos 3° = 0.9986$$
$$\cos 4° = 0.9976$$
$$\cos 5° = 0.9962$$

With the preceding values for the sine and cosine ratios, we may proceed with further calculations. For this purpose we may employ two types of formulas closely related to one another. These are:

$$\sin (A + B) = \sin A \cos B + \cos A \sin B$$
and $$\cos (A + B) = \cos A \cos B - \sin A \sin B$$

Thus, $\sin 6° = \sin (3° + 3°) = 2 \sin 3° \cos 3° = 2 \cdot 0.0524 \cdot 0.9986 = 0.1046$; $\sin 7°$ may be computed as $\sin (1° + 6°)$, or $\sin (2° + 5°)$ or as $\sin (3° + 4°)$.

We may go on computing the numerical values of the sine and cosine ratios of the angles up to and including those of 15°. As soon as we reach 15°, we may use the numerical value of $\sin 30°$ which is 0.5000 and of $\cos 30°$ which is $\sin 60°$ or 0.8860. For angles between 30° and 45° we will make use of the formulas:

$$\sin (A - B) = \sin A \cos B - \cos A \sin B$$
and $$\cos (A - B) = \cos A \cos B + \sin A \sin B$$

TABLE OF NUMERICAL VALUES OF SINES AND COSINES

	Angle (°)	Sine	Cosine	Angle (°)	
	0	0	1.0000	90	
	1	0.0175	0.9998	89	
R	2	0.0349	0.9994	88	
	3	0.0523	0.9986	87	
E	4	0.0698	0.9976	86	
	5	0.0872	0.9962	85	
A	6	0.105	0.995	84	
	7	0.122	0.993	83	
D	8	0.139	0.990	82	
	9	0.156	0.988	81	
	10	0.174	0.985	80	
	11	0.191	0.982	79	
D	12	0.208	0.978	78	
	13	0.225	0.974	77	
O	14	0.242	0.970	76	
	15	0.259	0.966	75	
W	16	0.276	0.961	74	
	17	0.292	0.956	73	
N	18	0.309	0.951	72	
	19	0.326	0.946	71	
	20	0.342	0.940	70	
	21	0.358	0.934	69	
	22	0.375	0.927	68	
	23	0.391	0.921	67	
	24	0.407	0.914	66	
	25	0.423	0.906	65	
	26	0.438	0.899	64	
	27	0.454	0.891	63	
	28	0.470	0.883	62	R
	29	0.485	0.875	61	
	30	0.500	0.866	60	E
	31	0.515	0.857	59	
	32	0.530	0.848	58	A
	33	0.545	0.839	57	
	34	0.559	0.829	56	D
	35	0.574	0.819	55	
	36	0.588	0.809	54	
	37	0.602	0.799	53	
	38	0.616	0.788	52	U
	39	0.629	0.777	51	
	40	0.643	0.766	50	P
	41	0.656	0.755	49	
	42	0.669	0.743	48	
	43	0.682	0.731	47	
	44	0.695	0.719	46	
	45	0.707	0.707	45	
	Angle	Cosine	Sine	Angle	

Thus, sin 16° may be computed as sin (30° − 14°). It may be also computed as sin (8° + 8°). Sin 35° may be computed as sin (30° + 5°), as sin (18° + 17°), or as sin (45° − 20°). The reader may select any other combination of angles for which the numerical values of the sine and cosine ratios have previously been computed.

Because of the relations sin A = cos $(90° − A)$ and cos A = sin $(90° − A)$, the entire table of numerical values of the sine and cosine ratios may be written as soon as the calculations reach 45°. Thus, for example, sin 75° = cos 15°, and cos 75° = sin 15°.

The calculation of the tangent ratios is performed by means of the formula

$$\frac{\sin A}{\cos A} = \tan A$$

For simplicity and because our calculations may have introduced discrepancies, our table should be written so that all the numerical values are given with not more than three significant digits. Up to and including the angles of 5° our table will have four decimals. Beyond that point, however, three decimals should be recorded. The table of the numerical values of the sine, cosine, and tangent ratios is given on page 142.

Distances Between Two Places
Without Trigonometry

A method for computing the distance between two points on the surface of the earth was originally proposed by the Russian mathematician P. L. Tschebyscheff in 1869. This method does not require the use of trigonometry.

Suppose that we have two points on the surface of the earth, and their locations are given by their latitudes and longitudes respectively. Let these two points be denoted by A and B, and the latitudes and the longitudes be denoted as follows:

Point	Latitude	Longitude
A	a_1	b_1
B	a_2	b_2

We shall assume:

1. The earth is spherical in shape and has a radius of 4,000 miles.
2. The distance between the two points is measured along an arc which joins these two points.
3. The differences of the latitudes, on the one hand, and the differences of the longitudes, on the other hand, together with the arc which joins the two points A and B, form a triangle on the surface of the earth that is, on the surface of a sphere (see Figure 61).

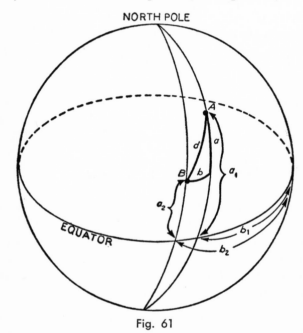

Fig. 61

4. Finally, for the purposes of the development of the rule, we shall assume that this triangle on the surface of the sphere is small.

We will denote the difference between the latitudes $(a_1 - a_2)$ by the symbol a and the difference between longitudes $(b_1 - b_2)$ by the symbol b. Assume that the latitude of this position is 45°. If the triangle is very small, then we can apply a simplified distance formula (which is an approximation, however). This formula, denoting the distance along the arc by the symbol d and the radius of the earth by R, is

$$d = R\sqrt{a^2 + \cos^2 45° \cdot b^2}$$

If we substitute the value of $\cos 45° = \dfrac{\sqrt{2}}{2}$, we have

$$d = R\sqrt{a^2 + \left(\frac{\sqrt{2}}{2}\right)2b^2}$$

Simplifying the expression under the radical sign, and using the approximate relation $\sqrt{2} = 1.4$, we obtain

$$d = \tfrac{1}{2}R\sqrt{(1.4b)^2 + (2a)^2}$$

Now we must find an expression which will approximate the square root, so the actual extraction of the square root may be avoided. The expression which we are seeking will *approximate* the square root as follows:

$$\sqrt{(1.4b)^2 + (2a)^2} = M(1.4b) + N(2a)$$

In other words, we must find the numerical values for M and N which will give the best approximation of the square root, while the extraction is not actually performed.

Before we can proceed with the derivation of our rule, we must find the values of the symbols M and N. We shall assume that the numerical values of the symbols M and N are associated with the trigonometric expression,

$$P(x) = M \cos x + N \sin x$$

whose numerical value is assumed to be very close to unity (that is, to 1). To obtain the correct expressions for the numerical values of M and N, we must select that form for the expression of $P(x)$ which deviates from unity the least. Then our approximation to the root will be the best.

Assume that the value of the angle x is such that it is located somewhere between the values of two angles α and β. This is denoted symbolically as follows:

$$\alpha \leq x \leq \beta, \quad \text{where} \quad \beta - \alpha < \pi, \quad (\pi = 180°)$$

The symbol $<$ denotes the meaning of "less than" and the symbol $\leq$ denotes the meaning of "less than or equal to."

Let us denote the difference between $P(x)$ and unity by the symbol D. We have then the following possible relations between $P(x)$ and unity:

$$1 - P(\alpha) = 1 - (M \cos \alpha + N \sin \alpha) = D$$

$$P\left(\frac{\alpha + \beta}{2}\right) - 1 = N \cos \frac{\alpha + \beta}{2} + M \sin \frac{\alpha + \beta}{2} - 1 = D$$

$$1 - P(\beta) = 1 - (M \cos \beta + N \sin \beta) = D$$

The three equations above have three unknowns, namely, M, N, and D. After solving these three equations for the unknowns, we obtain the following expressions for them:

$$M = \frac{\cos \dfrac{\alpha + \beta}{2}}{\cos^2 \dfrac{\beta - \alpha}{4}}, \qquad N = \frac{\sin \dfrac{\alpha + \beta}{2}}{\cos^2 \dfrac{\beta - \alpha}{4}},$$

$$D = \tan^2 \frac{\beta - \alpha}{4}$$

In order to reduce the amount of error in the computation of the square root, when an approximate expression is employed, we must select the numerical values of M and N so that they produce the desired effect. For this purpose we must examine the numerical values of $2a$ and of $1.4b$. If $2a$ is less than $1.4b$, we compute the numerical values of M and N respectively by taking $\alpha = 0°$, and $\beta = 45°$. If, on the other hand, $2a$ is greater than $1.4b$, we compute the numerical values of M and N respectively by taking $\alpha = 45°$ and $\beta = 90°$.

If $\alpha = 0°$ and $\beta = 45°$, that is, when $(2a)$ is less than $(1.4b)$, we obtain the following numerical values:

$$M = \frac{\cos 22.5°}{\cos^2 11.25°} = 0.9605$$

$$N = \frac{\sin 22.5°}{\cos^2 11.25°} = 0.3978$$

$$D = \tan^2 11.25° = 0.0396$$

Then the expression

$$\sqrt{(1.4b)^2 + (2a)^2} = 0.9605(1.4b) + 0.3978(2a)$$

approximates the square root. The error in this approximation is symbolized by the numerical value of D which is taken in relation to unity or 1. Since D can be taken as the relative error (the amount of error per each unit of measure), the relative error is 0.0396. The per cent of error between the approximation and the square root cannot, then, exceed 4 per cent.

The expression for the distance between the two points A and B on the earth's surface assumes the form

$$d = \tfrac{1}{2}R[0.3978(2a) + 0.9605(1.4b)]$$

where $2a$ is less than $1.4b$.

The differences of the latitudes and of the longitudes are expressed in angular measures. We, however, are interested in linear measures. To obtain these we must translate the angular measures, as expressed in the numerical values of the differences a and b, and express the numerical values in minutes. Furthermore, since our linear measure is expressed in terms of the radius of the earth R and in miles, we must translate the angular measures in terms of the radius of the earth's sphere. An arc of a circle (the radius of this circle is the same as the radius of the earth's sphere, that is, R) contains 3437.75 minutes. When a and b are expressed in minutes, we must divide them each by 3437.75. We then have

$$d = \frac{1}{2}R\left[\frac{0.3978(2a)}{3437.75} + \frac{0.9605(1.4b)}{3437.75}\right]$$

After substituting the numerical value of R (4,000) and performing the indicated arithmetic computations, we arrive at

$$d = 0.2316(2a) + 0.5588(1.4b), \quad \text{when} \quad 2a < 1.4b$$

If $2a > 1.4b$, α equals $45°$ and β is equal to $90°$, the numerical values for M, N, and D are:

$$M = \frac{\sin 22.5°}{\cos^2 11.25°} = 0.3978$$

$$N = \frac{\cos 22.5°}{\cos^2 11.25°} = 0.9605$$

$$D = \tan^2 11.25° = 0.0396$$

When these numerical values are inserted into the expression for the approximation of the square root, the formula becomes

$$d = \tfrac{1}{2}R[0.9605(2a) + 0.3978(1.4b)]$$

where $2a$ is greater than $1.4b$.

After changing the angular measures into linear measures and performing all the arithmetic computations, we have

$$d = 0.5588(2a) + 0.2316(1.4b), \quad \text{when} \quad 2a > 1.4b$$

To reduce the arithmetic computations required in computing the distance between two points on the surface of the earth, when the locations of these points are given in terms of their respective longitudes and latitudes, we shall introduce further simplifications. Let us replace the coefficients 0.5588 and 0.2316 by

$$0.5588 = 0.6 \quad \text{approximately}$$
and
$$0.2316 = 0.25 \text{ approximately}$$

The two formulas arrived at above then become

$$d = 0.25(2a) + 0.6(1.4b), \quad \text{when} \quad 2a < 1.4b$$
and
$$d = 0.6(2a) + 0.25(1.4b), \quad \text{when} \quad 2a > 1.4b$$

The final statements in terms of formulas enable us to formulate a rule for computing the distance between two points on the surface of the earth, when the locations of these points are given in terms of the respective latitudes and longitudes. Tschebyscheff's original rule was stated in a different form and in different terms. The statement of the rule is:

1. Determine the difference of the latitudes and express this difference in minutes.
2. Obtain the difference of the longitudes and express this difference in minutes.
3. Multiply the difference of the latitudes by 2.
4. Multiply the difference of the longitudes by 1.4.
5. Note which of the products thus obtained is greater and which is smaller.
6. Multiply the greater product by 0.6.
7. Multiply the smaller product by 0.25.
8. Add the two products which were obtained in 6 and 7 above. This sum will give the distance in miles between the two points.

Let us apply the foregoing formulas in computing the distance between New York City and Chicago and between New York City and Kansas City. Chicago is at latitude 41°50′N and longitude 87°38′W; New York City is at latitude 40°42′N and longitude 74°00′W. The difference in latitude is 1°08′ or 68′, and the difference in longitude is 13°38′ or 818′. In this case we apply the formula used when $2a < 1.4b$. Since $818 \cdot 1.4 = 1145.2$, we have

$$d = 0.25 \cdot 136 + 0.6 \cdot 1145 = 34 + 687 = 721$$

The distance between Chicago and New York City is 724 air miles. The error in our computation is 3 miles. The predicted error should not exceed 4 per cent or 29 miles.

Kansas City is at latitude 39°05′N and longitude 94°38′W. The difference between the latitude of Kansas City and

New York City is $1°37'$ or $97'$, and the difference between the longitudes is $20°38'$ or $1238'$. Since

$$97 \cdot 2 = 194 \quad \text{and} \quad 1238 \cdot 1.4 = 1733.2$$
$$d = 0.25 \cdot 194 + 0.6 \cdot 1733.2 = 48.5 + 1039.92 = 1088.42$$

The distance between New York City and Kansas City is 1117 air miles. The error in our computation is 29 miles, while the expected error of 4 per cent is 45 miles.

The reader may perform other computations and determine the distances between other points on the earth's surface.

Chapter 13

COMPUTATIONS
WITHOUT
NUMBERS

Graphical Computations

Arithmetic operations, that is, operations with numbers, are often long and tedious. Although it is true that many of these operations may now be performed by machine, few of us own or know how to use slide rules or computing machines. Graphical computations require very simple equipment. A pencil, a pair of compasses, and a ruler are all the instruments which are required.

Graphical computations are based on a very simple principle. Numbers may be represented by straight line segments. The length of a given straight line segment corresponds to a given number. The straight line segments are drawn in accordance with rules which obey the properties of geometric figures. Such drawings are called "constructions." After the specific construction is completed, there is a final straight line segment. This final straight line segment is measured by means of the ruled straightedge, and the measure of this final straight line segment is the required numerical result of the performed operations.

Although use of a ruled straightedge violates the classical geometric principle requiring that the straightedge be unmarked, graphical computations are practical. They are not concerned with pure geometric constructions. The con-

structions used in graphical computations are *means* and
not ends of the operations.

Graphical computations are never exact, however, but
exact results are not necessary in most practical situations.
Drawing straight lines which exactly represents given
numbers is impossible. There are many reasons for the lack
of exactness in graphical computations. Rulers, no matter
how fine they are, never contain divisions of equal magni-
tude. When we measure line segments with rulers, we depend
on our eyesight, and human eyes are extremely unreliable
instruments.

The single important element in all graphical constructions is an arbitrarily selected length of a straight line segment which is accepted as the unit or considered equal to 1.
All numbers are represented by straight line segments whose
lengths are expressed in terms of this unit. Thus, the number
5 is represented by a straight line segment which is five
times as long as the arbitrarily selected unit of length. The
unit may be of any length.

Graphical Addition

Suppose that several quantities are to be added and that
these quantities are stated in terms of numbers. We select
a unit of length. Then the quantities are expressed in terms
of the selected unit of length (see Figure 62). After all the
quantities have been represented by straight line segments,

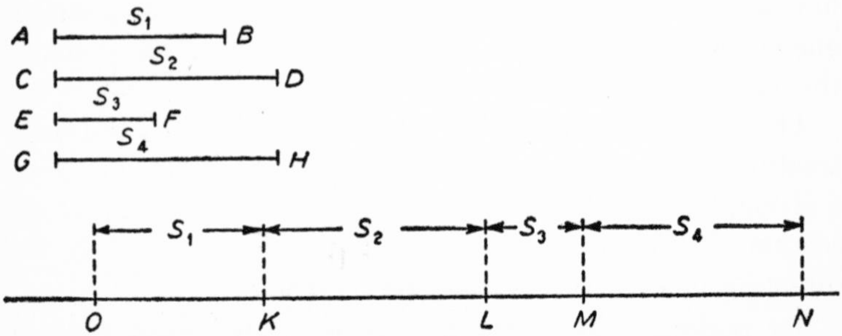

Fig. 62

we draw a straight line and place a mark 0 at some point on this straight line. Then, by means of compasses, we mark off the straight line segment OK which is equal in length to the straight line segment $S_1 = AB$. One foot of the compass is placed at O, while the other foot of the compasses makes the mark K. With another opening of the compasses, we mark off the straight line segment KL which is equal in length to the straight line segment $S_2 = CD$. We place one foot of the compasses at the point K, and mark off the point L with the other foot. The same procedure is repeated with the straight line segments $S_3 = EF$ and $S_4 = GH$. Thus we obtain the sum

$$ON = OK + KL + LM + MN$$
$$= AB + CD + EF + GH = S_1 + S_2 + S_3 + S_4$$

The length of the straight line segment is measured in terms of the selected unit of length.

Graphical Subtraction

Subtraction, when performed graphically, also involves marking off straight line segments on a straight line. The straight line segments which are to be subtracted are, however, marked off in the direction opposite to the direction in which the added straight line segments are marked. If the terminal point of the added line segments is to the right of the initial point, the terminal point of the subtracted segments is to the left of the initial point. Whether straight line segments are added or subtracted, the initial point of one straight line segment is placed at the terminal point of the preceding segment.

The rule for graphically performed addition and subtraction is: If addition is performed in one direction along a straight line, subtraction is performed in the opposite direction. If the direction of addition is upward, then the direction of subtraction must be downward.

To perform the subtraction $S_1 - S_2$, we must draw a straight line and mark a point O. To the right of this point O we must then mark off the straight line segment $OE = S_1 = AB$. With the point E, the terminal point of the straight line segment OE, as the initial point of the segment which is to be subtracted, we mark off the segment EF. This results in the straight line segment

$$OF = OE - EF = S_1 - S_2 = AB - CD$$

Addition and subtraction of straight line segments may be performed in one set of continuous operations, but it is important to remember that the direction of subtraction is opposite to the direction of addition. The example below illustrates the addition and subtraction of straight line segments. The required operations are represented symbolically as $S_1 + S_2 - S_3 + S_4 - S_5$ (see Figure 63).

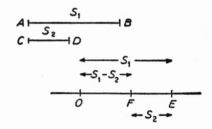

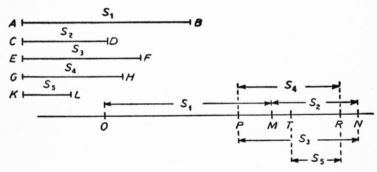

Fig. 63

From the point O we mark off (to the right) $OM = S_1 = AB$
From the point M we mark off (to the right) $MN = S_2 = CD$
From the point N we mark off (to the left) $NP = S_3 = EF$

From the point P we mark off (to the right) $PR = S_4 = GH$
From the point R we mark off (to the left) $RT = S_5 = KL$

The straight line segment

$$OT = OM + MN - NP + PR - RT = AB + CD$$
$$- EF + GH - KL = S_1 + S_2 - S_3 + S_4 - S_5$$

Graphical Multiplication

Graphical multiplication is based on the property of similar triangles which have a common vertex. Reference to the vertex is made to describe the procedure which is employed in graphical multiplication. When two triangles are similar, their corresponding sides are proportional. Thus (see Figure 64), if the triangles ABC and ADE are similar, then we have the proportion

$$\frac{AD}{AE} = \frac{AB}{AC}$$

From this we see $AD \cdot AC = AB \cdot AE$.

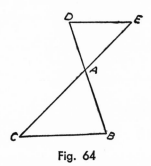

Fig. 64

If AD is our arbitrarily selected unit, that is, $AD = 1$, then $AB \cdot AE = AC$. This shows us the procedure which is employed in graphical multiplication.

We draw any angle (see Figure 64). Starting with the vertex A, we mark off a straight line segment AD which is equal to our arbitrarily selected unit. On the same line, we mark off a straight line segment AB which is the first factor and is expressed in terms of the unit AD. On the other side of the angle we mark off the straight line segment AE which is the second factor and is also expressed in terms of our arbitrarily selected unit AD. We join the points D and E with the straight line DE. Through the point B we draw the straight line BC parallel to the straight line DE. The straight line AC is the required product.

If all the factors are positive, the drawing (Figure 64) is used. If one of the two factors is negative, the drawing (Figure 65) is used. The factor AB is negative, and it is marked off in the opposite direction of the unit AD. The product AC is negative. Figure 65 shows that the product of a positive and a negative quantity is negative.

Graphical Division

Graphical division is also based on the properties of similar triangles. In Figure 65 the triangle ABC and AED are

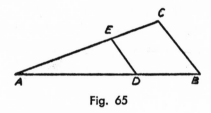

Fig. 65

similar. We have then that

$$\frac{AD}{AE} = \frac{AB}{AC}$$

Since, in this case, our arbitrarily selected unit is $AE = 1$, we have

$$AD = \frac{AB}{AC}$$

Thus, the numerical value of AD is equal to the quotient of AB and AC.

To divide graphically we draw an angle, and starting with the vertex, mark off $AE = 1$ on one side (see Figure 65).

On the same side we start with the vertex and mark off AC which is the divisor. On the other side of the angle, starting with the vertex, we mark off AB which is the dividend. Join the points B and C with the straight line BC. Through the point E we draw the straight line ED parallel to the straight line BC. The straight line segment AD is the required quotient.

Graphical multiplication and graphical division may be also performed by means of the proportion obtained by considering the property of two intersecting straight lines cut by two parallel straight lines. This proportion is

$$\frac{AE}{EC} = \frac{AD}{DB}$$

Using AD as the arbitrarily selected unit, $EC = AE \cdot DB$. If AE is the arbitrarily selected unit, we have $EC = \dfrac{DB}{AD}$.

Graphical Raising to a Power

To raise a number to a power, we can make use of the properties of similar triangles (see Figure 66), modifying the construction somewhat.

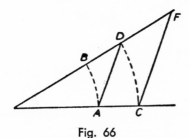

Fig. 66

Draw an angle, and on each of its sides, mark off the straight line segments OA and OB which are the arbitrarily selected units. That is, $OA = OB = 1$. On both sides of the angle we also mark off OC and OD so that $OC = OD$. We join the points A and D with the straight line AD. Through the point C, we draw the straight line CF parallel to the straight line AD.

Since the triangles OAD and OFC are similar, we have the proportion

$$\frac{OA}{OD} = \frac{OC}{OF}$$

and from this we see that $OA \cdot OF = OD \cdot OC$. Because $OA = 1$ and $OC = OD$,

$$OF = OC^2$$

The numerical value of the straight line segment OF, as measured in terms of the arbitrarily selected unit OA, is equal to the square of the numerical value of OC which is measured in terms of the same arbitrarily selected unit OA.

We may construct the square of a straight line segment in another way (see Figure 67). Again, starting with the vertex, we mark off $OA = OB = 1$, our arbitrarily selected

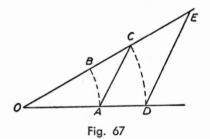

Fig. 67

unit, on the sides of the angle. On the side OB we mark off the line segment OC which is to be squared. With OC as a radius, we mark off the straight line segment $OD = OC$ on side OA. By joining the points A and C, we get the straight line AC. Through the point D we draw the straight line DE parallel to the straight line AC. The straight line segment $OE = OC^2$.

Because the triangles OAC and ODE are similar, the proportion is

$$\frac{OE}{OC} = \frac{OD}{OA}$$

Since $OA = 1$ and $OC = OD$, $OE = OC^2$.

The same process may be continued (see Figure 68). With OE as a radius we mark off the line $OF = OE$ on the side OA. We draw the straight line OG parallel to the straight line AC (or DE). The triangles AFG and OAC are similar, and the proportion is

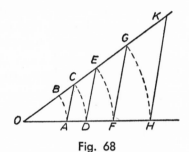

Fig. 68

$$\frac{OG}{OC} = \frac{OF}{OA}$$

Since $OA = 1$, $OG = OC \cdot OF$. Because $OF = OC^2$,

$$OG = OC^3$$

If we use OG as a radius and mark off the line $OH = OG$ on the straight line OA and draw the straight line HK parallel to AC (or ED or FG), we have two similar triangles OAC and OHK. We then have the proportion

$$\frac{OK}{OC} = \frac{OG}{OA}$$

Since $OA = 1$, $OK = OC \cdot OG$. But $OG = OC^3$; so

$$OK = OC^4$$

This process may be carried out indefinitely to obtain successively the powers of OC, that is, OC^5, OC^6, OC^7, and so on.

Figure 69 shows that the process may also be performed by moving toward the vertex. To do this we mark off the arbitrary unit $OA = OB = 1$ on the sides of the angle. On the side OB, we mark off OC and join the points A and C with the straight line AC. Through the point B we draw the straight line BD parallel to the straight line AC. The triangles OAC and OBD are similar, and the proportion is

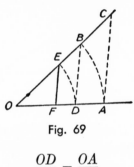

Fig. 69

$$\frac{OD}{OB} = \frac{OA}{OC}$$

Since $OA = OB = 1$, $OD = \dfrac{1}{OC}$

On the straight line OB, using the radius OD, we mark off the point E so that $OE = OD$. Through the point E we draw the straight line EF parallel to the straight line BD (or AC). The triangles OEF and OAC are similar, and the proportion is

$$\frac{OF}{OE} = \frac{OD}{OB}$$

But $OB = 1$, and $OE = OD$. Then

$$OF = OD^2$$

Since $OD = \dfrac{1}{OC}$, $OF = \dfrac{1}{OC^2}$

This procedure may be carried out indefinitely to obtain the successive powers of $\dfrac{1}{OC}$.

Another Graphical Method of Raising to a Power

Graphical raising to a power may also be performed by employing a geometric property which is associated with a right triangle. If a perpendicular to the hypotenuse is drawn from the vertex of the right angle C of the triangle ABC, $AD \cdot DB = CD^2$ (see Figure 70). The numerical value of

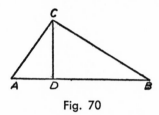

Fig. 70

the perpendicular CD is the mean proportional of the numerical values of the straight line segments AD and DB. This relation is derived from the fact that the right triangles ACD and DBC are similar. From this we obtain the proportion

$$\frac{AD}{CD} = \frac{CD}{DB}$$

and $AD \cdot DB = CD^2$.

Let us draw two perpendicular straight lines OX and OY (see Figure 71). On the straight line OX, starting from the point O, mark off the straight line segment OA which is an arbitrarily selected unit. Starting from O, on the straight line OY, mark off the straight line segment OB which is expressed in terms of the unit of measure OA. Join the points A and B with the straight line AB. At the point B draw the straight line BC perpendicular to the straight line AB.

The triangle ABC is a right triangle, and the straight line OB is perpendicular to the hypotenuse AC. The length of the straight line OB is a mean proportional between the lengths of the straight lines OA and OC. This can be stated

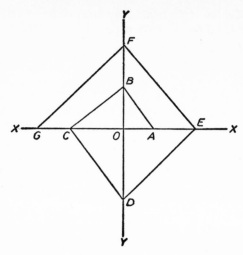

Fig. 71

as $OB^2 = OA \cdot OC$. But, since OA is the arbitrarily selected unit which is equal to 1,

$$OC = OB^2$$

This means that the numerical value of the measure of the straight line segment OC, when it is expressed in terms of the arbitrarily selected unit of measure OA, is equal to the square of the numerical value of the straight line segment OB, when it is also expressed in terms of OA.

A perpendicular to BC at the point C will intersect the straight line OY at the point D. We then have the right triangle BCD in which the length of the straight line OC is a mean proportional between the lengths of OB and OD. In other words, $OC^2 = OB \cdot OD$. Since $OC = OB^2$, then $OC^2 = OB^4$. The expression $OC^2 = OB \cdot OD$, when rewritten, becomes $OB^4 = OB \cdot OD$. The result of dividing this expression by OB is

$$OD = OB^3$$

A perpendicular to the straight line CD at the point D produces a right triangle CDE. In this triangle the length of the straight line OD is a mean proportional between the lengths of OC and OE, and $OD^2 = OC \cdot OE$. But $OD = OB^3$ and $OC = OB^2$. Since $OD^2 = (OB^3)^2 = OB^6$, then $OB^6 = OB^2 \cdot OE$. When both sides of the expression are divided by OB^2, the result is

$$OE = OB$$

This process may be carried out indefinitely to obtain the successive powers of OB, OB^5, OB^6, OB^7, and so on.

The procedure described above may be reversed. Instead of drawing the perpendicular to the straight line AB at the point B, we may draw the perpendicular at the point A (see Figure 72). This perpendicular will intersect the straight line OY in the point H. The triangle ABH is a right triangle, and the length of the straight line segment OA is a mean proportional between the lengths of the straight line segments OB and OH. Then $OA^2 = OB \cdot OH$. Since the straight line segment OA is the arbitrary selected unit which is equal to 1, $OB \cdot OH = 1$, and

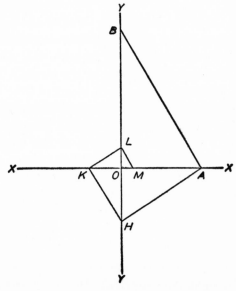

Fig. 72

$$OH = \frac{1}{OB}$$

If we draw a perpendicular to the straight line segment AH at the point H, the perpendicular will intersect the straight line OX in the point K. We then have the right triangle AHK. In this triangle, the length of the straight line segment OH is a mean proportional between the lengths of the straight line segments OA and OK. Then $OH^2 = OA \cdot OK$. Because $OA = 1$ and $OH = \frac{1}{OB}$,

$$OK = \frac{1}{OB^2}$$

A perpendicular to the straight line segment HK drawn at the point K will intersect the straight line OY in the point L. The triangle HKL is a right triangle, and the length of the straight line segment OK is a mean proportional between the lengths of the straight line segments OH and OL. Then $OK^2 = OH \cdot OL$. Because $OK = \frac{1}{OB^2}$, $OK^2 = \frac{1}{OB^4}$, and $OH = \frac{1}{OB}$, simplification produces

$$OL = \frac{1}{OB^3}$$

Continuation of the process described here results in the successive powers of $\frac{1}{OB}$.

The Graphical Extraction of the Square Root

The property of the mean proportional may also be applied to the graphical extraction of square root. However, one more property of the right triangle must be used. Thus far, we have used the property of the perpendicular which was drawn from the vertex of the right angle to the hypotenuse. The length of this perpendicular is the mean proportional between the lengths of the two portions BD and

DA of the hypotenuse AB (see Figure 73). Now we will also employ the following property: a right triangle can be inscribed in a semicircle, and the hypotenuse of this triangle is the diameter of the circle.

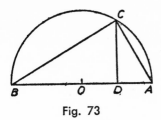

Fig. 73

To extract the square root of a straight line segment BD which is expressed in terms of an arbitrarily selected unit AD, we proceed as follows. We construct a straight line segment $AB = AD + BD$. Taking the straight line segment as a diameter, we draw a semicircle. To do this, we bisect the straight line segment AB. Using the point O, which is the midpoint of the straight line segment AB, as the center of the circle, and the straight line segment OA as the radius, we draw the semicircle. Next we erect the perpendicular CD at the point D on the diameter AB. The straight line segment CD is the required square root of BD. This can be noted from the following. Since the length of the straight line segment CD is the mean proportional between the lengths of the straight line segments AD and BD, $CD^2 = BD \cdot AD$. Because AD is the arbitrarily selected unit and equal to 1, $CD^2 = BD$ and

$$CD = \sqrt{BD}$$

Graphical extraction of a square root may be performed successively as shown in Figure 74.

After obtaining the first square root $C_1D = \sqrt{B_1D}$, we proceed as follows. With C_1D as a radius we mark off the straight line segment $B_2D = C_1D = \sqrt{B_1D}$ on the diameter AB. The problem then is similar to the one we confronted

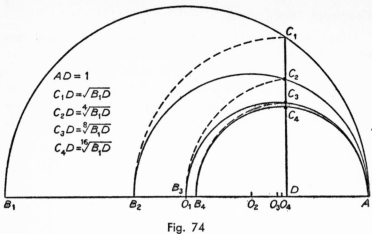

Fig. 74

when we extracted the square root of the straight line segment BD. In this case, however, our diameter is AB_2 on which we have to erect a semicircle. The arbitrarily selected unit is still AD. The midpoint of the straight line segment AB_2 is the center O_2 of the new semicircle. This semicircle will intersect the straight line C_1D in the point C_2, and the straight line segment C_2D is the square root of the straight line segment B_2D, that is, $C_2D = \sqrt{B_2D}$. But $B_2D = C_1D = \sqrt{B_1D}$. Then, since C_2D is the square root of the square root of B_1D we find that

$$C_2D = \sqrt[4]{B_1D}$$

Having obtained C_2D, we use it as a radius and mark off the straight line segment $B_3D = C_2D$. After drawing the semicircle on the diameter AB_3, we obtain $C_3D = \sqrt{B_3D}$. From the information which was gleaned thus far, we finally derive

$$C_3D = \sqrt[8]{B_1D}$$

We may continue this process indefinitely and obtain the square root of the square root of the square root of the square root, and so on, of the straight line segment B_1D.

Graphical Trigonometry

Graphical computations may be applied with equal success to trigonometry, especially to the numerical values of the trigonometric ratios of a given angle.

Suppose that we have an angle α. We select an arbitrarily chosen unit $OA = 1$. With this unit and the angle α we construct a right triangle OAB, where the angle AOB is equal to α (see Figure 75).

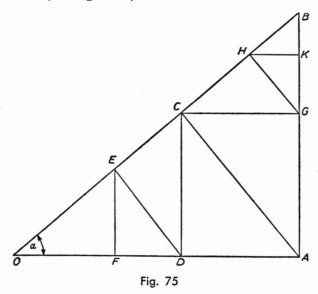

Fig. 75

Next we draw the perpendicular AC to the hypotenuse OB. Then

$$OC = \cos \alpha \quad \text{and} \quad AC = \sin \alpha$$

From the point C, we draw the perpendicular CD to the side OA. Since the triangle OCA is a right triangle, the length of the straight line segment OC is the mean proportional between the lengths of the straight line segment OD and OA, and

$$\frac{OD}{OC} = \frac{OC}{OA}$$

Since $OA = 1$ and $OC = \cos \alpha$,

$$OD = \cos^2 \alpha$$

We then draw the perpendicular DE to the hypotenuse of the right triangle OCD. The length of the straight line segment OD is the mean proportional between the lengths of the straight line segments OE and OC, that is,

$$\frac{OE}{OD} = \frac{OD}{OC}$$

From this we see that

$$OE = \frac{OD^2}{OC}$$

Since $OD = \cos^2 \alpha$ and $OC = \cos \alpha$,

$$OE = \cos^3 \alpha$$

In a similar manner we can learn that $OF = \cos^4 \alpha$. If we continue to draw perpendiculars which approach the vertex of the angle α, we may obtain the expressions for numerical values of $\cos^5 \alpha$, $\cos^6 \alpha$, and so on, in terms of the lengths of the straight line segments which are the perpendiculars.

Since the triangles OAC and ACD are similar,

$$\frac{AD}{AC} = \frac{AC}{OA}$$

Because $OA = 1$ and $AC = \sin \alpha$,

$$AD = \sin^2 \alpha$$

Furthermore, since $AD + DO = AO = 1$, we see that

$$\sin^2 \alpha + \cos^2 \alpha = 1$$

When we draw the straight line segment CG parallel to OA, we get

$$CG = AD = \sin^2 \alpha$$

If we draw the perpendicular GH to the hypotenuse BC of the right triangle BCG, the similarity of the triangles HCG and ACG will show us that

$$\frac{HG}{CG} = \frac{CG}{AC}$$

From the similarity of the triangles HCG and OAC, we learn that

$$\frac{HG}{CG} = \frac{AC}{AO}$$

When we see that $CG = AD = \sin^2 \alpha$, $AC = \sin \alpha$, and $AO = 1$, we discover that

$$HG = \sin^3 \alpha$$

In a similar manner we learn that $HK = \sin^4 \alpha$.

If we continue to draw the perpendiculars which more closely approach the vertex B, we get the expressions for $\sin^5 \alpha$, $\sin^6 \alpha$, and so on.

The triangle AOC shows us that $CD^2 = OD \cdot DA$. Since $OD = \cos^2 \alpha$ and $DA = \sin^2 \alpha$,

$$CD = \sin \alpha \cdot \cos \alpha = \tfrac{1}{2} \sin 2\alpha$$

The difference $OD - AD$ yields the expression

$$OD - AD = \cos^2 \alpha - \sin^2 \alpha = \cos 2\alpha$$

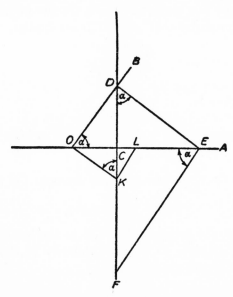

Fig. 76

The graphical computation of the tangent ratios is performed as follows. Angle $AOB = \alpha$ (see Figure 76). Starting with the point O on the side OA, we mark off a straight line segment OC which is our arbitrarily selected unit equal to 1. At the point C we draw a straight line perpendicular to the straight line OA. From the right triangle COD, the straight line segment represents the numerical value of $\tan \alpha$ (in terms of the unit $OC = 1$). If we draw a perpendicular at the point D to the straight line OD, the perpendicular will intersect the straight line OA at the point E. Then $CE = \tan^2 \alpha$. After drawing the perpendicular EF, we see that the straight line segment $CF = \tan^3 \alpha$. This procedure may be continued indefinitely to obtain the successive values (in terms of straight line segments) for $\tan^4 \alpha$, $\tan^5 \alpha$, and so on.

To obtain the expressions for the cotangent ratios in terms of straight line segments, we draw the perpendicular OK at the point O. We then see that $CK = \cot \alpha$. The perpendicular KL yields the straight line segment $CL = \cot^2 \alpha$. If we continue drawing perpendiculars which approach the point C, we get the successive expressions, in terms of straight line segments, for $\cot^3 \alpha$, $\cot^4 \alpha$, and so on.

Concluding Remarks

The graphical methods for computation described in this chapter should not be considered exact. However, it should be understood that with care in drawing and with careful handling of the measuring ruler, tolerably acceptable numerical results may be secured.

Whenever a result is obtained in terms of a straight line segment, the result should be translated into numerical values by applying the arbitrarily selected unit of measure to it. The numerical value should be stated in terms of this unit of measure. If the unit of measure which was arbitrarily selected is a gradation on the ruler, for example $\frac{1}{16}$ inch, then the measure of the final graphical result should be stated in terms of a sixteenth of an inch.

Chapter 14

SOME REMARKABLE NUMBERS

The Persistent 9

When any two-digit number is written in reverse order, the new number is also a two-digit number. If the digits in a two-digit number are different, the difference between the number and its "reverse" possesses a remarkable property; it is always evenly divisible by 9. For example, the reverse of 74 is 47, and $74 - 47 = 27$. The reverse of 83 is 38, and $83 - 38 = 45$. The reverse of 91 is 19, and $91 - 19 = 72$. All of these differences, 27, 45, and 72, can be divided by 9 with no remainder.

This fact may be verified by writing a general expression for a two-digit number as $10a + b$. The reverse of this number is then written as $10b + a$. The difference of these two numbers is $10a + b - (10b + a) = 10a + b - 10b - a$ and is equal to

$$9a - 9b = 9(a - b)$$

This result indicates that the difference between a two-digit number and its reverse is always divisible with no remainder by 9.

It should be noted that the difference between a two-digit number and its reverse can never be greater than 81. In other words, these differences may be

$$
\begin{array}{lll}
1 \cdot 9 = 9 & 4 \cdot 9 = 36 & 7 \cdot 9 = 63 \\
2 \cdot 9 = 18 & 5 \cdot 9 = 45 & 8 \cdot 9 = 72 \\
3 \cdot 9 = 27 & 6 \cdot 9 = 54 & 9 \cdot 9 = 81
\end{array}
$$

The sum of any such difference and its "reverse" is always equal to 99. Thus, $27 + 72 = 99$, $45 + 54 = 99$, and $72 + 27 = 99$.

Three-Digit Numbers and 99

When any three-digit number is written in reverse order, the new number is also a three-digit number. If at least two of the three digits are different, the difference between the number and its "reverse" is always evenly divisible by 99. For example, the reverse of 635 is 536, and $635 - 536 = 99$. The reverse of 841 is 148, and $841 - 148 = 693$. The reverse of 512 is 215, and $512 - 215 = 297$. Each of these differences is divisible by 99 with no remainder.

This fact may be verified if we write a general expression for a three-digit number as $100a + 10b + c$. The reverse of this number is then written as $100c + 10b + a$. The difference of these two numbers is

$$100a + 10b + c - (100c + 10b + a)$$
$$= 100a + 10b + c - 100c - 10b - a$$

and is equal to

$$99a - 99c = 99(a - c)$$

This result indicates that the difference between any three-digit number and its reverse is always divisible with no remainder by 99. This difference is also always divisible with no remainder by 9 and 11, because $99 = 9 \cdot 11$.

The difference between a three-digit number and its reverse cannot ever be greater than 891. In other words, the differences may be

$$\begin{array}{lll} 1 \cdot 99 = 99 & 4 \cdot 99 = 396 & 7 \cdot 99 = 693 \\ 2 \cdot 99 = 198 & 5 \cdot 99 = 495 & 8 \cdot 99 = 792 \\ 3 \cdot 99 = 297 & 6 \cdot 99 = 594 & 9 \cdot 99 = 891 \end{array}$$

The sum of any such difference and its "reverse" is always equal to 1,089. Thus, $297 + 792 = 1,089$, $495 + 594 = 1,089$.

In other words, the sum of a difference and its "reverse" is always equal to $11 \cdot 99 = 1,089$.

This property of the difference between a three-digit

number and its reverse may form the basis for a trick. Ask someone to select any three-digit number but not tell you the number. Ask that this number be written in reverse order. When the difference of these two numbers is obtained (you are not to be told what this difference is), ask that this difference be written in reverse order and added to the original difference. Then announce that this sum is 1,089. One warning is in order, however. The original number must be such that its "reverse" be different from the original number. Thus, for example, the selected number should not be 212, 252, 464, 717, or 939.

Some Numerical Curiosities

When a number is multiplied by itself the operation is symbolically indicated by writing the indicator "2" to the right above the number. Thus, $2 \cdot 2$ may be written as 2^2, and $53 \cdot 53$ may be written as 53^2. This is read as: "Two squared" and "Fifty-three squared." The squares of the following numbers may be easily remembered:

$$11^2 = 121$$
$$111^2 = 12,321$$
$$1,111^2 = 1,234,321$$
$$11,111^2 = 123,454,321$$
$$111,111^2 = 12,345,654,321$$
$$1,111,111^2 = 1,234,567,654,321$$
$$11,111,111^2 = 123,456,787,654,321$$
$$111,111,111^2 = 12,345,678,987,654,321$$

The numbers 121, 12,321, 1,234,321, 123,454,321, and so on, possess additional interesting properties. The sums of the digits of these numbers are

$$1 + 2 + 1 = 4 = 2^2$$
$$1 + 2 + 3 + 2 + 1 = 9 = 3^2$$
$$1 + 2 + 3 + 4 + 3 + 2 + 1 = 16 = 4^2$$
$$1 + 2 + 3 + 4 + 5 + 4 + 3 + 2 + 1 = 25 = 5^2$$
$$1 + 2 + 3 + 4 + 5 + 6 + 5 + 4 + 3 + 2 + 1 = 36 = 6^2$$
$$1 + 2 + 3 + 4 + 5 + 6 + 7 + 6 + 5 + 4 + 3 + 2 + 1 = 49 = 7^2$$
$$1 + 2 + 3 + 4 + 5 + 6 + 7 + 8 + 7 + 6 + 5 + 4 + 3 + 2 + 1 = 64 = 8^2$$
$$1 + 2 + 3 + 4 + 5 + 6 + 7 + 8 + 9 + 8 + 7 + 6 + 5 + 4 + 3 + 2 + 1 = 81 = 9^2$$

The same numbers 121, 12,321, 1,234,321, 123,454,321, and so on, may be represented in the form of the following fractions:

$$121 = \frac{22 \cdot 22}{1 + 2 + 1}$$

$$12,321 = \frac{333 \cdot 333}{1 + 2 + 3 + 2 + 1}$$

$$1,234,321 = \frac{4,444 \cdot 4,444}{1 + 2 + 3 + 4 + 3 + 2 + 1}$$

$$123,454,321 = \frac{55,555 \cdot 55,555}{1 + 2 + 3 + 4 + 5 + 4 + 3 + 2 + 1}$$

$$12,345,654,321 = \frac{666,666 \cdot 666,666}{1 + 2 + 3 + 4 + 5 + 6 + 5 + 4 + 3 + 2 + 1}$$

$$1,234,567,654,321 = \frac{7,777,777 \cdot 7,777,777}{1 + 2 + 3 + 4 + 5 + 6 + 7 + 6 + 5 + 4 + 3 + 2 + 1}$$

$$123,456,787,654,321 = \frac{88,888,888 \cdot 88,888,888}{1 + 2 + 3 + 4 + 5 + 6 + 7 + 8 + 7 + 6 + 5 + 4 + 3 + 2 + 1}$$

$$12,345,678,987,654,321 = \frac{999,999,999 \cdot 999,999,999}{1 + 2 + 3 + 4 + 5 + 6 + 7 + 8 + 9 + 8 + 7 + 6 + 5 + 4 + 3 + 2 + 1}$$

The Peculiarities of 37

The number 37 is a prime number, that is, it is divisible by 1 and by itself only. It has no other divisors. There are, however, more interesting properties of this number.

If we multiply 37 by the number 3 or by multiples of 3, up to and including 27, we always obtain products which are written with the same digit. Thus:

$$37 \cdot 3 = 111 \quad 37 \cdot 6 = 222 \quad 37 \cdot 9 = 333$$
$$37 \cdot 12 = 444 \quad 37 \cdot 15 = 555 \quad 37 \cdot 18 = 666$$
$$37 \cdot 21 = 777 \quad 37 \cdot 24 = 888 \quad 37 \cdot 27 = 999$$

The product of 37 and the sum of its digits is equal to the sum of the cubes of its digits. Thus:

$$37 \cdot (3 + 7) = 3^3 + 7^3$$
$$37 \cdot 10 = 27 + 343$$
$$370 = 370$$

If we add the squares of the digits in the number 37 and subtract from this sum the product of these digits, the difference is equal to 37. That is

$$3^2 + 7^2 - 3 \cdot 7 = 37$$
$$9 + 49 - 21 = 37$$
$$37 = 37$$

The Budget Director's Nightmare

At a meeting of a certain Legislative Committee on Budgets and Appropriations, the Budget Director testified concerning the Budget prepared by his department. The legislators took one look at the total amount of money required and decided to effect some drastic economies. "Cut the total to one-third," he was told. "By the way, how much will that be?" he was asked. "Well," replied the Budget Director, "this will require some division. I think, I should take it back and put it through our electronic computors. You know, we do not want any mistakes. In my younger years I was a county judge. I am a bit rusty on my arithmetic."

One of the members of the Legislative Committee was an accountant. "Look here," he told the Budget Director, "the digit on the extreme left of your total is 7. Take this digit and place it on the extreme right, and you get exactly one-third of your total."

"But you will have to check the result by multiplying it by 3," replied the Budget Director. "I am not sure I can rely on my ability to do this correctly either. No, I think I will put it through our newest calculators."

What was the Budget Director's total?

We know that the digit on the extreme left was 7. Then the number was of the form $7abcd \ldots n$, where a, b, c, $d, \ldots, n$ are symbols for the digits 0, 1, 2, 3, 4, 5, 6, 7, 8, or 9. The division by 3 is then indicated by the relation

$$7abcd \ldots n \div 3 = abcd \ldots n7$$

When we divide 7 by 3 we obtain a quotient 2 and a remainder 1. Thus $a = 2$. With the remainder 1 and the number 2 we have 12. Dividing 12 by 3 we obtain a quotient 4. Thus, $b = 4$. Dividing 4 by 3 we obtain a quotient 1 and a remainder 1. Thus, $c = 1$. With the remainder 1 and the number 1 we have 11. Dividing 11 by 3 we obtain a quotient 3 and a remainder 2. Thus, $d = 3$. With the remainder 2 and the number 3 we have 23. Dividing 23 by 3 we obtain a quotient 7 and a remainder 2. This process is carried out until we finally obtain a quotient 7 and a remainder 0. The entire process of division is reproduced below:

The consecutive dividends	The remainder	The quotient	The digits of the number
7	1	2	7
12	0	4	2
4	1	1	4
11	2	3	1
23	2	7	3
27	0	9	7
9	0	3	9
3	0	1	3
1	1	0	1
10	1	3	0
13	1	4	3
14	2	4	4
24	0	8	4
8	2	2	8
22	1	7	2
17	2	5	7
25	1	8	5
18	0	6	8
6	0	2	6
2	2	0	2
20	2	6	0
26	2	8	6
28	1	9	8
19	1	6	9
16	1	5	6
15	0	5	5
5	2	1	5
21	0	7	1

Thus, the Budget Director's number was

7,241,379,310,344,827,586,206,896,551

If you divide that number by 3, you will find that one-third of it is, in fact,

$$2,413,793,103,448,275,862,068,965,517$$

and that the 7 has been moved to the extreme right.

Actually, this is the smallest number which will satisfy the conditions of the problem. If we use this number as a period of a repeating decimal fraction, we obtain a general expression for this number as follows:

7241379310344827586206896551 . . .
7241379310344827586206896551 . . .
7241379310344827586 . . .

It may be pointed out here that dividing a number by 3, if a digit on the extreme left of the number is moved to the extreme right, may be extended to numbers which begin with any other digit, if the sequence of the digits is the same as the sequence in the Budget Director's number. Examine the sequence of the numbers which follow:

1,034,482,758,620,689,655,172,413,793
2,068,965,517,241,379,310,344,827,586
3,103,448,275,862,068,965,517,241,379
4,137,931,034,482,758,620,689,655,172
5,172,413,793,103,448,275,862,068,965
6,206,896,551,724,137,931,034,482,758
8,275,862,068,965,517,241,379,310,344
9,310,344,827,586,206,896,551,724,137

PROBLEMS

5. Write the number 1 using three 5's.
6. Write 0 (zero) using three 5's.
7. Write the number 2 using three 5's.
8. Write the number 31 using five 3's.
9. Write the number 100 using five 3's.
10. Write the number 10 using five 3's.

11. Write the number 100 using the digits 1, 2, 3, 4, 5, 6, 7, 8, and 9 (each digit to be used once and once only) and the symbols "+" and "—" three times only.

12. If we move the digit which is on the extreme left of a number to the extreme right, the number remains unchanged. What is the number?

13. There are nine numbers which will be divided by 2 if the digit on the extreme left of each number is moved to the extreme right. What are these numbers?

14. There are nine numbers which will be divided by 4 if the digit on the extreme left of each number is transposed to the extreme right. What are these numbers?

15. What are the nine numbers which are divided by 5 when the first digit is made the last?

16. Find the nine numbers which are divided by 6 when the first digit becomes the last.

17. You can find one-seventh of nine different numbers by moving the digit on the left to the right. What are these numbers?

18. If the digit on the left is moved to the extreme right, nine numbers will be divided by 8. What are these numbers?

19. What nine numbers are divided by nine when the first digit of each number is made the last?

SOLUTIONS TO PROBLEMS

CHAPTER ONE

1.

VI

2.

XII

3.

ONE

4.

5.

6.

7.

8.

9.

10.

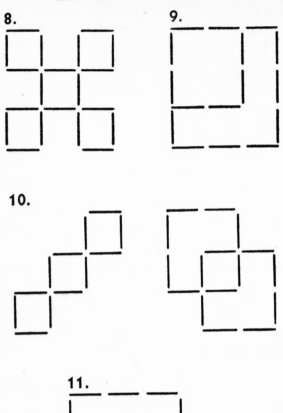

11.

12.

13. **14.** **15.**

16. **17.**

18.

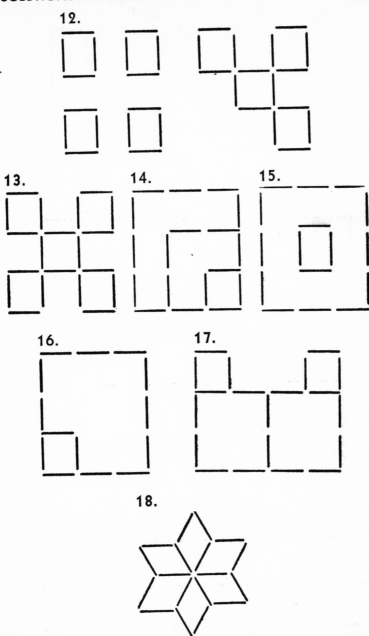

19.

20.

21.

22.

23.

24.

25.

26.

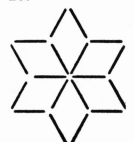

27.

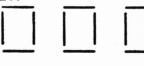

28.

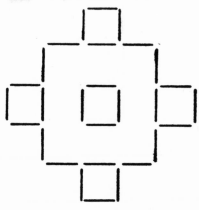

29.

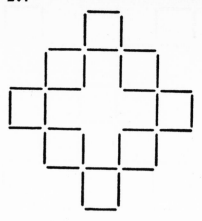

30.

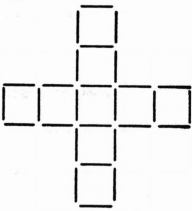

31.

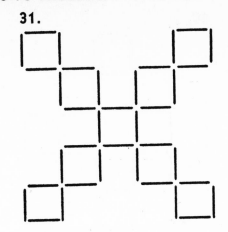

32.

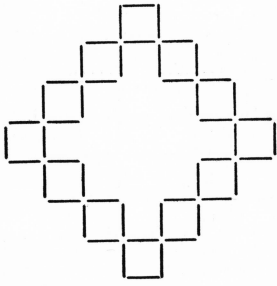

33.

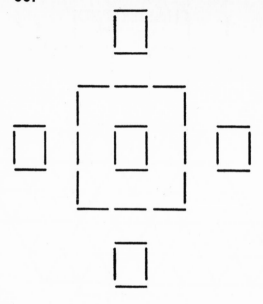

34. **35.**

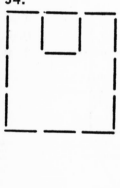

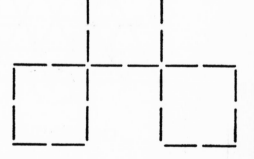

CHAPTER TWO

1.

```
11 gallons  11 4 4 9 9 2 2 7 7 0 0 5 5 10 10 3 3 8 8 1 1 6 6 11
 7 gallons   0 7 2 2 0 7 4 4 0 7 6 6 1  1  0 7 3 3 0 7 5 5  0  0
 5 gallons   0 0 5 0 2 2 5 0 4 4 5 0 5  0  1 1 5 0 3 3 5 0  5  0
```

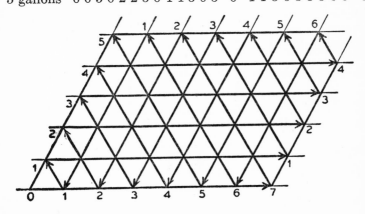

2.

```
7 gallons  7 2 2 5 5 0 0 3 3 6 6 1 1 4 4 7
5 gallons  0 5 2 2 0 5 4 4 1 1 0 5 3 3 0 0
3 gallons  0 0 3 0 2 2 3 0 3 0 1 1 3 0 3 0
```

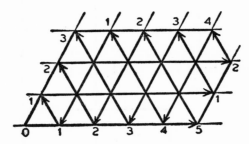

CHAPTER THREE

1. 1,100,010,000.

2. 19.013.

3. 1,000,000,000,001,010,001,110,101.

4. $1 + 2 + 4 + 8 + 16 + 32 + 64 + 128 + 256 + 239.$

5. $1 + 2 + 4 + 8 + 16 + 32 + 64 + 128 + 256 + 512$
$+ 177.$

CHAPTER FOUR

1. 111,100,101,010;

2. 111,111,110,001,110,110,100.

3. 100,010,000,000,110,101,110;

4. 101,111,100,000,111,001,111,000,010.

5. 11,111,111,111,100,011,000,000,000,000,111;

6. 10,100,101,111,010,100,000,010,011,000.

7. 11,000,010.01101 . . . ;

8. 101,001,000.011 . . .

9. 3,653,720,423,256,013;

10. 75,203,575,231,764.

11. 1,101,111,110,011,100,101,010,111,001,000,000,111,
011,101,110,001,010;

12. 111,000,000,000,101,010,001,000,100,010,110,101,111,
010,100,011,001,101,010,111,011,011,100,001,010,110,
001,101,001,100.

CHAPTER FIVE

4.

Weight	Left Side of Balance	Right Side of Balance	Weight	Left Side of Balance	Right Side of Balance
1	1	0	21	1+1+1+9+9	0
2	1+1	0	22	1+1+1+1+9+9	0
3	1+1+1	0	23	9+9+9	1+1+1+1
4	1+1+1+1	0	24	9+9+9	1+1+1
5	9	1+1+1+1	25	9+9+9	1+1
6	9	1+1+1	26	9+9+9	1
7	9	1+1	27	9+9+9	0
8	9	1	28	1+9+9+9	0
9	9	0	29	1+1+9+9+9	0
10	1+9	0	30	1+1+1+9+9+9	0
11	1+1+9	0	31	1+1+1+1+9+9+9	0
12	1+1+1+9	0	32	9+9+9+9	1+1+1+1
13	1+1+1+1+9	0	33	9+9+9+9	1+1+1
14	9+9	1+1+1+1	34	9+9+9+9	1+1
15	9+9	1+1+1	35	9+9+9+9	1
16	9+9	1+1	36	9+9+9+9	0
17	9+9	1	37	1+9+9+9+9	0
18	9+9	0	38	1+1+9+9+9+9	0
19	1+9+9	0	39	1+1+1+9+9+9+9	0
20	1+1+9+9	0	40	1+1+1+1+9+9+9+9	0

5.

Weight	Left Side of Balance	Right Side of Balance	Weight	Left Side of Balance	Right Side of Balance
1	1	0	21	3+9+9	0
2	3	1	22	1+3+9+9	0
3	3	0	23	9+9+9	1+3
4	1+3	0	24	9+9+9	3
5	9	1+3	25	1+9+9+9	3
6	9	3	26	9+9+9	1
7	1+9	3	27	9+9+9	0
8	9	1	28	1+9+9+9	0
9	9	0	29	3+9+9+9	1
10	1+9	0	30	3+9+9+9	0
11	3+9	1	31	1+3+9+9+9	0
12	3+9	0	32	9+9+9+9	1+3
13	1+3+9	0	33	9+9+9+9	3
14	9+9	1+3	34	1+9+9+9+9	3
15	9+9	3	35	9+9+9+9	1
16	1+9+9	3	36	9+9+9+9	0
17	9+9	1	37	1+9+9+9+9	0
18	9+9	0	38	3+9+9+9+9	1
19	1+9+9	0	39	3+9+9+9+9	0
20	3+9+9	1	40	1+3+9+9+9+9	0

6.

Weight	Left Side of Balance	Right Side of Balance	Weight	Left Side of Balance	Right Side of Balance
1	1	0	21	27	3+3
2	3	1	22	1+27	3+3
3	3	0	23	27	1+3
4	1+3	0	24	27	3
5	3+3	1	25	1+27	3
6	3+3	0	26	27	1
7	1+3+3	0	27	27	0
8	3+3+3	1	28	1+27	0
9	3+3+3	0	29	3+27	1
10	1+3+3+3	0	30	3+27	0
11	3+3+3+3	1	31	1+3+27	0
12	3+3+3+3	0	32	3+3+27	1
13	1+3+3+3+3	0	33	3+3+27	0
14	27	1+3+3+3	34	1+3+3+27	0
15	27	3+3+3+3	35	3+3+3+27	1
16	1+27	3+3+3+3	36	3+3+3+27	0
17	27	1+3+3+3	37	1+3+3+3+27	0
18	27	3+3+3	38	3+3+3+3+27	1
19	1+27	3+3+3	39	3+3+3+3+27	0
20	27	1+3+3	40	1+3+3+3+3+27	0

7.

Weight	Left Side of Balance	Right Side of Balance
1	1	0
2	1+1	0
3	1+1+1	0
4	1+1+1+1	0
5	9	1+1+1+1
6	9	1+1+1
7	9	1+1
8	9	1
9	9	0
10	1+9	0
11	1+1+9	0
12	1+1+1+9	0
13	1+1+1+1+9	0
14	27	1+1+1+1+9
15	27	1+1+1+9
16	27	1+1+9
17	27	1+9
18	27	9
19	1+27	9
20	1+1+27	9

Weight	Left Side of Balance	Right Side of Balance
21	1+1+1+27	9
22	1+1+1+1+27	9
23	27	1+1+1+1
24	27	1+1+1
25	27	1+1
26	27	1
27	27	0
28	1+27	0
29	1+1+27	0
30	1+1+1+27	0
31	1+1+1+1+27	0
32	9+27	1+1+1+1
33	9+27	1+1+1
34	9+27	1+1
35	9+27	1
36	9+27	0
37	1+9+27	0
38	1+1+9+27	0
39	1+1+1+9+27	0
40	1+1+1+1+9+27	0

8. (*a*)   1,121,011;
   (*b*)   1,001,002,012;
   (*c*)   12,002,100,222.

9. (*a*)   417;   (*b*)   1,093;   (*c*)   5,740.

10.

1 one	30 three-six	100 six-six
2 two	31 three-six one	101 six-six one
3 three	32 three-six two	102 six-six two
4 four	33 three-six three	103 six-six three
5 five	34 three-six four	104 six-six four
	35 three-six five	105 six-six five
10 one-six		
11 one-six one	40 four-six	110 six-six-one-six
12 one-six two	41 four-six one	
13 one-six three	42 four-six two	
14 one-six four	43 four-six three	
15 one-six five	44 four-six four	
	45 four-six five	
20 two-six		
21 two-six one	50 five-six	
22 two-six two	51 five-six one	
23 two-six three	52 five-six two	
24 two-six four	53 five-six three	
25 two-six five	54 five-six four	
	55 five-six five	

11.   122,023,311,232,022,121.

12.   11,001,010,010,001,010,011,111,001,000,100,100,000,
   111,110,010,001.

13.   3,253,057,625.

14.   1,100,011,111,100,110,110,110,111,001,000,100,111,
   111,000,001,011,101,101,010,111,111,000,001,001,
   111,111.

15.   22,120,121,210,211,111,000,111.

16.   2,741.

17.   382,574,055,424.

18.   220,101,000,002,021,210,212,022,210,002,012,202, 000,010,111,100,010,211.

CHAPTER SIX

1.   12,11,03,21.

2.   1,03,14,10,12.

3.   13,02,10,00.

4.

$$
\begin{array}{r}
1,13 \\
13 \\
\hline
2,04 \\
4,00 \\
\hline
10,04 \\
14,00 \\
\hline
1,04,04
\end{array}
$$

$$
\begin{array}{rcl}
10 \cdot 3 &=& 1,10 \\
10 \cdot 10 &=& 2,10 \\
10 \cdot 1,00 &=& 10,00 \\
\hline
 & & 14,00
\end{array}
$$

5.   1,21,13.

6.   4,01,01.

7.   20,10,10.

8.   24,34,22,21.

9.   14,01,11,13,03.

10.   1,04,11,11,10.

11.   15,01,11,03.

12.   2,12,02,11,12,12.

13.   **14.**   **15.**

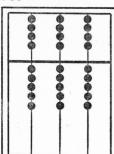 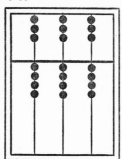 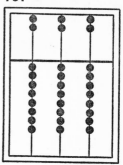

CHAPTER SEVEN

1. (*a*)   Odd;   (*b*)   Even;   (*c*)   Even;
    (*d*)   Odd;   (*e*)   Even;   (*f*)   Odd.

2. (*a*)   Not divisible;   (*b*)   Not divisible;
    (*c*)   Divisible;   (*d*)   Not divisible.

3. (*a*)   Not divisible;   (*b*)   Not divisible;
    (*c*)   Not divisible.

4. (*a*)   Not divisible;   (*b*)   Not divisible
    (*c*)   Not divisible.

CHAPTER NINE

1.   **2.**

 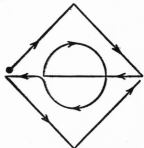

3. Impossible.

4.

5.

6.

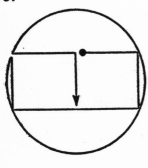

7.

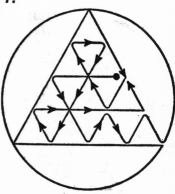

8.

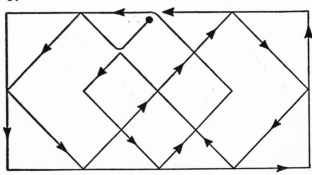

9.

10.

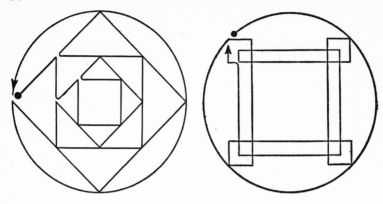

11.

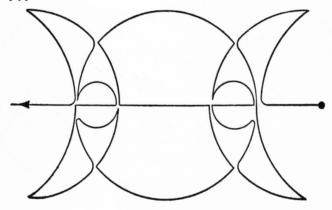

12.

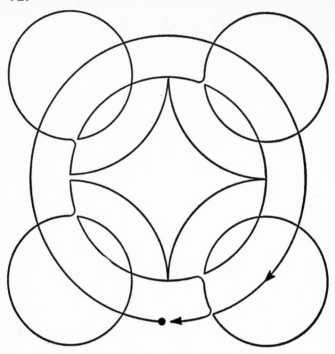

CHAPTER ELEVEN

1.   4 turns.

2. $3\frac{1}{2}$ turns.

3.   3 turns.

4.   2 turns.

5.

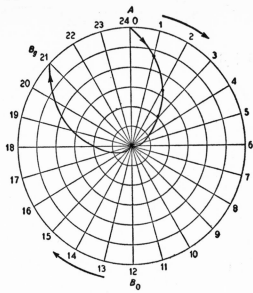

6.

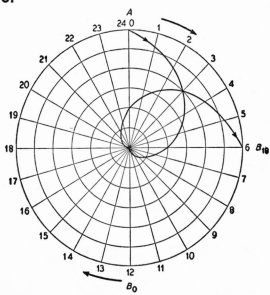

CHAPTER FOURTEEN

1. $33 + 3 + \dfrac{3}{3} = 37.$

2. $\dfrac{333}{3 \times 3} = 37.$

3. $n = \dfrac{2a}{a - 2}.$

a	3	4	5	6
n	6	4	$\frac{10}{3}$	3

4. $n = \dfrac{a}{2a - 1}$

a	1	2	3	4
n	1	$\frac{1}{3}$	$\frac{3}{5}$	$\frac{4}{3}$

5. $5^{5-5}.$

6. $(5 - 5)\,5 = 0, \quad \dfrac{5 - 5}{5} = 0.$

7. $\dfrac{5 + 5}{5} = 2.$

8. $3^3 + 3 + \dfrac{3}{3} = 31, \quad 33 - 3 + \dfrac{3}{3} = 31,$

$33 - \dfrac{3 + 3}{3} = 31.$

9. $(33 \times 3) + \dfrac{3}{3} = 100.$

10. $\dfrac{(3 \times 3 \times 3) + 3}{3} = 10, \quad \dfrac{3^3}{3} + \dfrac{3}{3} = 10.$

11. $123 - 45 - 67 + 89 = 100.$

12.   Any number consisting of the same digits, as, for
example, 222, 4,444.

13.   105,263,157,894,736,842,
210,526,315,789,473,684,
315,789,473,684,210,526,
421,052,631,578,947,368,
526,315,789,473,684,210,
631,578,947,736,842,105,
736,842,105,263,157,894,
842,105,263,157,894,736,
947,368,421,052,631,578.

14.   102,564,
205,128,
307,692,
410,256,
512,820,
615,384,
717,948,
820,512,
923,076.

15.
102,040,816,326,530,612,244,897,959,183,673,469,387,755,
204,081,632,653,061,224,489,795,918,367,346,938,877,551,
306,122,448,979,591,836,734,693,877,551,020,408,163,265,
408,163,265,306,122,448,979,591,836,734,693,877,551,020,
510,204,081,632,653,061,224,897,959,183,673,469,387,755,
612,244,897,959,183,673,469,387,755,102,040,816,326,530,
714,285,
816,326,530,612,244,897,959,183,673,469,387,755,102,040,
918,367,346,938,775,510,204,081,632,653,061,224,489,795.

16.

1,016,949,152,542,372,881,355,932,203,389,830,508,474,576,271,186,440,677,966,
2,033,898,305,084,745,762,711,864,406,779,661,016,949,152,542,372,881,355,932,
3,050,847,457,627,118,644,067,796,610,169,491,525,423,728,813,559,322,033,898,
4,067,796,610,169,491,525,423,728,813,559,322,033,898,305,084,745,762,711,864,
5,084,745,762,711,864,406,779,661,016,949,152,542,372,881,355,932,203,389,830,
6,101,694,915,254,237,288,135,593,220,338,983,050,847,457,627,118,644,167,796,
7,118,644,167,796,610,169,491,525,423,728,813,559,322,033,898,305,084,745,762,
8,135,593,220,338,983,050,847,457,627,118,644,067,796,610,169,491,525,423,728,
9,152,542,372,881,355,932,203,389,830,508,474,576,271,186,440,677,966,101,694.

17. 1,014,492,753,623,188,405,797,
2,028,985,507,246,376,811,594,
3,043,478,260,869,565,217,391,
4,057,971,014,492,753,623,188,
5,072,463,768,115,942,028,985,
6,086,956,521,739,130,434,782,
7,101,449,275,362,318,840,579,
8,115,942,028,985,507,246,376,
9,130,434,782,608,695,652,173.

18. 1,012,658,227,848,
2,025,316,455,696,
3,037,974,683,544,
4,050,632,911,392,
5,063,291,139,240,
6,075,949,367,088,
7,088,607,594,936,
8,101,265,822,784,
9,113,924,050,632.

19.

10,112.359.550,561,797,752.808,988,764,044.943,820,224,719,
20,224,719,101,123,595,505,617,977.528.089,887,640,449,438,
30,337,078,651,685,393,258,426,966.292,134,831,460,674,157,
40,449,438,202,247,191,011,235,955.056,179,775,280,898,876,
50,561,797,752,808,988,764,044,943,820,224,719,101,123,595,
60,674,157,303,370,786,516,853,932,584,269,662,921,348,314,
70,786,516,853,932,584,269,662,921,348,314,606,741,573,033,
80,898,876,404,494,382,022,471,910,112,359,550,561,797,752,
91,011,235,955,056,179,775,280,898,876,404,494,382,022,471.

INDEX

EASTER DATE CALENDAR

III

	00	01	02	03	04	05	06	07	08	09	10	11	12	13	14	15	16	17	18
Years in Centuries	19	20	21	22	23	24	25	26	27	28	29	30	31	32	33	34	35	36	37
	38	39	40	41	42	43	44	45	46	47	48	49	50	51	52	53	54	55	56
	57	58	59	60	61	62	63	64	65	66	67	68	69	70	71	72	73	74	75
	76	77	78	79	80	81	82	83	84	85	86	87	88	89	90	91	92	93	94
	95	96	97	98	99														

New Style Centuries	00	01	02	03	04	05	06	07	08	09	10	11	12	13	14	15	16	17	18
15	2	14	15	16	17	18	19	20	21	22	23	24	25	26	27	28	29	30	1
16	18	19	20	21	22	23	24	25	26	27	28	29	30	1	2	14	15	16	17
17	12	13	14	15	16	17	18	19	20	21	3	4	5	6	7	8	9	10	11
18	17	18	19	20	21	3	4	5	6	7	8	9	10	11	12	13	14	15	16
19	22	23	24	25	26	27	28	29	30	1	2	3	4	5	6	7	8	9	10
20	27	28	29	30	1	2	3	4	5	6	7	19	9	10	22	23	24	25	26
21	2	3	4	5	6	7	19	9	10	22	23	24	25	26	27	28	29	30	1

INSTRUCTIONS

1. In Table I of the Perpetual Calendar obtain the letter which is located at the intersection of the Column of the Years in Centuries with the Row of New Style Centuries.
2. In Table III of the Easter Date Calendar obtain the number which is located at the intersection of the Column of the Years in Centuries with the Row of the New Style Centuries.
3. In Table IV of the Easter Date Calendar obtain the number which is located at the intersection of the letter obtained in 1 above with the column of the row of the number obtained in 2 above. This number is the Easter Date.
4. The italic numbers refer to the month of March. The numbers printed in roman type give April dates.